Webb

MILLIKEN'S

GRADES 5-6

COMPLETE BOOK OF

Grammar REPRODUCIBLES

Over 110 Activities for Today's Differentiated Classroom

Compiled by: Sara Inskeep
Cover design: Logo Design Team
Page Layout: Janine M. Chambers

Printed in the United States of America

ISBN 978-1-4291-0463-0

MILLIKEN

P.O. Box 802 • Dayton, OH 45401
www.LorenzEducationalPress.com

How to Use This Book . . .

The activities in this book provide an excellent source of grammar practice for elementary students. The pages can be used as drill reinforcement or as independent instructional material and are designed to help motivate students to learn through a variety of exercises. The activities in this book are grouped by skill; these skills may overlap more than one grade level and should be used in ways that best meet each student's needs. The reproducibles are created so that a student can work with a minimum of supervision in a classroom or at home. Answer keys to all exercises have been provided in the back of the book.

EXTRA! EXTRA! When you see this symbol, be sure to check out the "extra" extension activity provided.

Table of Contents

Name _____ Date _____

Harry's hints:
     A **common noun** names **any person**, **place**, or **thing**.
Example: The **man** signed the **document**.
     A **proper noun** names a **particular person**, **place**, or **thing**. A proper noun begins with a **capital letter**.
Example: **John Hancock** signed the **Constitution of the United States**.

Circle the common nouns below and underline the proper nouns that should begin with a capital letter.

1. The famous face on the united states one-dollar bill is george washington.
2. Our first president lived at mount vernon as a young man.
3. He was a person who led our troops in the revolutionary war.
4. The portrait on the one-dollar bill was painted by gilbert stuart.
5. The artist painted three portraits of our first president.
6. The one unfinished portrait, called the athenaeum, is the most famous.

Harry's hints:
     An **abstract noun** cannot be touched. Honesty, truth, danger, respect, love, faith, and worry are examples of abstract nouns.
     A **concrete noun** can be touched or felt. A person, place, or thing is a concrete noun.

Circle the concrete nouns and underline the abstract nouns in the following sentences.
1. George Washington had a great deal of faith in our new country.
2. He did not want the power to be a king.
3. The truth was that he wanted to remain at his farm.
4. He learned about honesty from his parents, Augustine and Mary Washington.
5. He handled several dangers during the years of his presidency.
6. George Washington attended school in Virginia and had seriousness about his studies.
7. During the Revolutionary War, General Washington had great respect for his troops.
8. He developed many strategies during the war that were very clever.
9. Some stories about his honesty and strength may not be true.
10. Henry Lee wrote about his commander, ". . . first in war, first in peace, and first in the hearts of his countrymen."

CONCRETE POETRY
Concrete poetry creates an actual picture or shape. The poem's meaning comes from its shape as well as its words.

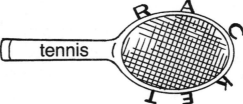

Create a concrete poem using any verb or noun. Use any number of words or sentences. There is no rhyme or other pattern. Make the shape of the poem relate to its subject matter.

Harry's hints:
    A **common noun** names any person, place, or thing.
Examples: trainer, zoo, bird cage
    A **proper noun** names a particular person, place, or thing.
Examples: Mr. Johns, St. Louis Zoo, World's Fair Bird Cage
    Begin each important word with a capital letter.

common
proper

In the following paragraph, underline the common nouns. Circle the proper nouns that should be capitalized.

susan and john arrived at the midtown movie theater too late to see the matinee. They decided to take a walk through forest park and see the animals at the st. louis zoo. It was labor day and they knew there would be a big crowd watching all the animals. The chimpanzee show was very popular.

Rewrite only the proper nouns correctly in the following list.

1. mississippi river _____
   _____
2. school _____
3. new york _____
4. boy _____
5. thanksgiving _____
6. city _____
7. lake _____

8. september _____
9. mayor _____
10. abraham lincoln _____
    _____
11. mexico _____
12. saturday _____
13. friend _____
14. dog _____

15. town _____
16. nbc network _____
    _____
17. airplane _____
18. jimmy carter _____
    _____
19. france _____
20. raincoat _____

Finish the crossword puzzle by changing each common noun into a proper noun.

ACROSS

  1. automobile
  3. president
  6. month
  9. city
  12. country
  13. special day
  14. city
  15. ocean

DOWN

  2. great lake
  4. day of the week
  5. continent
  7. author
  8. river
  10. breed of dog
  11. state

(crossword grid with letters: 1/2 D; T; 3 I 4 5; N; 6 R 7 I; O N; 8; 9 PHILADE 10 LPHIA; 11 12 E; I R; N; 13 N 14 L N; 15 C)

Name _____ Date _____

A **proper noun** names a **particular** person, place, or thing. It begins with a **capital letter**.

For each of the following common nouns, write an appropriate proper noun on the right.
Example: book—Bible

1. country _____   5. tree _____
2. poem _____   6. church _____
3. month _____   7. building _____
4. ocean _____   8. newspaper _____

For each of the following proper nouns, write an appropriate common noun on the right.
Example: Sphinx—statue

1. Nile _____   5. Tutankhamen _____
2. Egypt _____   6. Sahara _____
3. Africa _____   7. Mediterranean _____
4. Cairo _____   8. Arabic _____

In the following sentences, draw one line under the proper nouns and two lines under the common nouns.

1. Queen Nefertiti was a beautiful woman.
2. The Egyptian Museum has many fine treasures.
3. The Royal Scribes were favorites of the court.
4. Thebes was an important city in 1400 B.C.
5. The Rosetta Stone held the key to an ancient language.

In the following sentences, fill in the blanks with an appropriate proper or common noun.

1. The _____ Canal allows oceangoing _____ to sail between the Red Sea and the Mediterranean Sea.

2. _____ , the capital of Egypt, is the largest _____ in Africa.

3. _____ , which can go without water for a long time, are very useful in the _____ Desert.

Each of the following phrases is the name of a particular place. Write it correctly on the line at the right. Write a sentence containing each phrase on a separate paper. Add the correct capitalization and punctuation.

1. ministry of foreign affairs   _____
2. museum of modern art   _____
3. arab republic of egypt   _____
4. aswan high dam   _____
5. nile river valley   _____

Select a short paragraph from a book or story you have recently read. On another sheet of paper, make two lists: **common nouns** and **proper nouns**. Write down all of the nouns from your paragraph on the correct list.

Harry's hints:
A **singular noun** names **one** person, place, thing, or idea.
A **plural noun** names **more than one** person, place, thing, or idea.

Rules for Making Nouns Plural

Most plurals are made by adding **s**: girl—girls.
If the noun ends in **sh, ch, s, x**, or **z**, add **es**: box—boxes.
If the noun ends in a **vowel + y**, add an **s**: monkey—monkeys.
If the noun ends in a **consonant + y**, change y to **i** and add **es**: factory—factories.
If the noun ends in **f** or **fe**, change to **v** and add **es**: self—selves, knife—knives.

singular nou
plural nou

Write the plural of the following singular nouns.

1. circus _____
2. baby _____
3. flower _____
4. lunch _____
5. sky _____

6. penny _____
7. dress _____
8. dish _____
9. story _____
10. hobby _____

Write sentences using the plural form of these words:

house   church   shelf   butterfly   holiday

1. _____
2. _____
3. _____
4. _____
5. _____

Harry's hints:
Some nouns have the same spelling for the singular and plural forms: deer—deer, fish—fish.
Other nouns are formed irregularly; there is no rule: child—children.

Write the singular form of each plural noun. You may use a dictionary.

1. mice _____
2. women _____
3. geese _____
4. moose _____
5. men _____

6. teeth _____
7. feet _____
8. oxen _____
9. sheep _____
10. swine _____

Name _____ Date _____

In the following sentences, change the words in boldfaced type to plural nouns. Rewrite the sentences on the lines below.

1. Camel **taxi** carry tourists miles to the many **oasis**.

_____

2. **Thief** have stolen much treasure from ancient Egyptian **tomb**.

_____

3. The **child** wrote on papyrus with **brush**.

_____

4. Egyptians built their **city** on the **shore** of the Nile River.

_____

5. Artisans carved beautiful ornamental **box** with **knife**.

_____

6. **Horse**, **goose**, **sheep**, and **duck** were kept on the farm by Egyptian **family**.

_____

_____

Rewrite the following group of words so there is one possessive noun in each phrase. Example: the treasure of the tomb—the tomb's treasure

1. the hair of the lady   _____
2. the hair of the ladies   _____
3. the valley of the Kings   _____
4. the head of the Sphinx   _____
5. the art of the craftsmen   _____
6. the death of a hero   _____

In the following table, fill in the missing forms of the nouns. Follow the example.

Singular	Singular Possessive	Plural	Plural Possessive
Example: cat	cat's	cats	cats'
1. desert	_____	_____	_____
2. quarry	_____	_____	_____
3. woman	_____	_____	_____
4. dynasty	_____	_____	_____
5. flood	_____	_____	_____
6. document	_____	_____	_____

EXTRA!

On a separate sheet of paper, draw a picture of each of the following phrases: the **girls fish** and the **girl's fish**.

Teacher from Outer Space Needs Help!

A teacher from a galaxy far, far away has just landed on earth. He has never heard of plurals. (On his planet, there is only one of everything.) Help him learn these rules and apply them to the alien language. Write the number of the rule used in parentheses.

1. Add **s** to most nouns.
2. Add **es** to nouns ending in **ch, s, sh, x** or **z**.
3. Add **s** to nouns ending in a vowel and **y**.
4. Change **y** to **i** and add **es** to nouns ending in a consonant and **y**.
5. Add **s** to most nouns ending in a vowel and **o**.
6. Add **s** to many nouns ending in **f, fe,** or **ff**; some drop **f** or **fe** and add **ves**.

1. moof _____ ( )	9. vox _____ ( )	17. bobio _____ ( )
2. mnoar _____ ( )	10. quiff _____ ( )	18. chissiny _____ ( )
3. poray _____ ( )	11. poy _____ ( )	19. pruffy _____ ( )
4. xummy _____ ( )	12. nobo _____ ( )	20. quife _____ ( )
5. glif _____ ( )	13. glite _____ ( )	21. wus _____ ( )
6. shilp _____ ( )	14. mercat _____ ( )	22. pirpay _____ ( )
7. glish _____ ( )	15. molio _____ ( )	23. sliff _____ ( )
8. sofip _____ ( )	16. wertwez _____ ( )	24. troagy _____ ( )

Some noun plurals are irregular and must be memorized or looked up in a dictionary.

Change the nouns in boldfaced type below to their plural forms. It may be necessary to change other words to agree with the plurals.

1. I saw a **man** from outer space!

   I saw _____

2. He was trying to catch a **deer** to take aboard his spaceship.

   He was _____

3. My **brother-in-law** will help me if I decide to board the ship secretly.

   My _____

4. Before I got a cold **foot**, I found a good hiding spot.

   Before _____

5. I was as quiet as a **mouse** when I tiptoed aboard the craft.

   We _____

6. The alien added a **cupful** of an unknown substance to the tank.

   The _____

7. As the **ship** rose in the sky, I could see a **woman** and **child** below us.

   As the _____

8. I started to fear for my **life**.

   We _____

9. The alien **creature** may not like a **stowaway**.

   The _____

10. If I could make friends with the **creature** on this trip, I would be a **hero**.

    If we _____

EXTRA! Use the alien words to write a story about your experience on the planet where there was only one of everything! Before beginning your story, you might compose a dictionary of the alien words. Make up your own definitions.

Harry's hint:
Singular possessive shows ownership by **one** person, place, or thing. Add **'s** to the singular noun.
Example: The vest belonging to Harry is Harry's vest.

"Do you like my vest?"

Write the singular possessive of the following items:

1. the sweater of John _____
2. the fish of the boy _____
3. the chair of the teacher _____
4. the collar of the dog _____
5. the shore of the ocean _____

Harry's hint:
Plural possessive shows possession by **more than one** person, place, or thing.
If the plural noun ends in **s**, add an apostrophe: aunts—aunts'.
If the plural noun ends with any other letter, add **'s**: men—men's.

Write the plural possessive for each of the following singular possessives. You may need to make some of the things possessed plural.

1. flower's petals _____
2. car's horn _____
3. cow's milk _____
4. uncle's pipe _____
5. camera's lens _____
6. child's toy _____
7. lady's purse _____
8. pen's point _____
9. horse's saddle _____
10. brother's book _____

11. puppy's bone _____
12. bear's den _____
13. bench's legs _____
14. bike's wheel _____
15. shelf's edge _____
16. ax's handle _____
17. youth's game _____
18. egg's yolk _____
19. ostrich's feathers _____
20. mother's pie _____

Find the possessive nouns in the paragraph below. Write the singular possessive nouns in the first list, and write the plural possessive nouns in the second list.

It was a dark, windy night as we walked down the town's main street. The night was only different because it was Halloween. The trees' bark seemed to be the outline of monsters' faces. Everything startled us as we went up the Perkins' front stairs. The candles' reflection in the window made us walk very slowly. Our neighbor's house didn't appear to be the same pleasant home it normally was. The doorbell's ring sounded more like witches' screams. As the door opened slowly, we realized there was a large skeleton's shadow swinging against the door frame. We heard laughter in the back of the house's foyer. Needless to say, we were relieved to see our neighbor's friends dressed in costumes. What a night!

Singular Possessives

_____   _____

_____   _____

_____   _____

Plural Possessives

_____   _____

_____   _____

_____   _____

Name _____ Date _____

Harry loves babies. He thought the Noun Chart below would be a helpful way to remember different types of nouns. Follow the example to complete the chart.

"JUST ME"	"JUST THE TWO OF US"	"IT'S MINE!"	"THEY'RE OURS"
SINGULAR	PLURAL	SINGULAR POSSESSIVE	PLURAL POSSESSIVE
1. dog	dogs	dog's	dogs'
2. lady			
3. kite			
4. bird			
5. baby			
6. peach			
7. goose			
8. girl			
9. turkey			
10. family			
11. candy			
12. church			
13. dish			
14. fox			
15. woman			
16. sheriff			
17. mouse			
18. story			
19. key			
20. child			
21. boy			
22. knife			
23. box			
24. thief			

EXTRA! Another favorite activity of Harry's is to write "tongue twisters." Simply start a sentence, usually with a noun, and add as many words as possible that start with the same letter. Example: Harry hardly helped Hannah by holding her homework.
Write two of your own tongue twisters.

Name _____   Date _____

An **abstract noun** names something that cannot be seen or touched. A **concrete noun** is something real.

Put an **A** in front of each abstract noun and a **C** in front of each concrete noun. Use each noun in a sentence.

1. ___ dream _____
2. ___ pride _____
3. ___ ship _____
4. ___ sickness _____
5. ___ food _____
6. ___ sadness _____
7. ___ guitar _____
8. ___ fear _____

Change each verb or adjective into an abstract noun.

1. truthful   _____   6. fail   _____
2. quick   _____   7. silly   _____
3. honest   _____   8. faint   _____
4. ill   _____   9. helpful _____
5. please   _____   10. happy _____

At the end of the following paragraph, list all the abstract nouns.

Egyptians have long known the importance of families. Ancient paintings on tombs show the parents' joy in their children. They often took their children to the nearby rivers to fish and gather rushes. Sometimes, they gave a child a name like Beautiful Dawn as a remembrance of the day she was born. Today, family ties are still strong in the villages. Husbands and wives work in the fields all day. When the children get home from school, they all help with the chores. Many generations of a family often live in the same house.

_____

_____

Write a concrete noun for each of the following modifiers. Example: barking dog

1. running _____   6. twenty _____
2. beautiful _____   7. open _____
3. hungry _____   8. rare _____
4. tall _____   9. distinguished _____
5. easy _____   10. interesting _____

EXTRA! Select a short paragraph from a book or story you have recently read. On another sheet of paper, make two lists: **abstract nouns** and **concrete nouns**. Write down all of the nouns from your paragraph on the correct list.

Harry's hint:
    An **appositive** is a noun that helps explain or identify another noun that it follows. It may have modifiers with it. The appositive is separated from the rest of the sentence by **commas**.

Sometimes the appositives are not essential; they may be lifted out of the sentence. Other times they give necessary information.

Example: Dwight D. Eisenhower, *the 34th President of the United States,* was the Supreme Commander of the Allied Forces in World War II.

The italicized phrase in the example above is not essential to the meaning of the sentence.

Example: An American general, *Dwight D. Eisenhower,* was the Supreme Commander of the Allied Forces.

The italicized phrase in this example gives necessary information about the general.

In the following sentences, underline the appositives.

1. Dwight Eisenhower's family were members of River Brethren, a church that opposed war or any type of violence.
2. He entered West Point, the United States Military Academy, in 1911.
3. After graduation he married Mamie Geneva Doud, the daughter of a wealthy meat packer.
4. While serving in the Panama Canal Zone in 1941, his commander, Brigadier General Fox Connor, was certain that war was imminent.
5. On December 7, 1941, the date the Japanese attacked Pearl Harbor, Eisenhower was about to be appointed to the Pacific Ocean area.
6. During the war in Europe, Eisenhower worked on Operation Overlord, a plan to invade Europe.
7. On June 6, 1944, later called D-Day, the Allies invaded France to gain control of the area.
8. After the war, Eisenhower helped with demobilization, disbanding the armed services.
9. He was president of Columbia College for several years and wrote a book, *Crusade in Europe.*
10. Eisenhower was elected President of the United States in 1952 after campaigning against Adlai Stevenson, governor of Illinois.

Underline the appositives. (Some sentences do not have appositives.)
1. Many events occurred during the administrations of Dwight Eisenhower.
2. America entered the space age by launching its first satellite, Explorer I, in 1958.
3. The polio vaccine, developed by Jonas E. Salk, was given to school age children for the first time.
4. The first atomic-powered electricity was produced in the United States during this time.
5. "Atoms for Peace," a proposal to pool resources about atomic information for peaceful uses, was instigated by the President.

Appositives are useful for combining sentences. Use appositives to combine the following pairs of sentences.
1. Dwight Eisenhower was elected by a landslide in 1956. His nickname was "Ike". _____

_____

2. The St. Lawrence Seaway was opened in 1959. It is a man-made waterway to the interior of North America. _____

_____

3. Alaska and Hawaii joined the United States in 1959. They were the 49th and 50th states of the Union. _____

_____

Write two of your own sentences that contain appositives.

An **appositive** is a word or group of words that explain or mean the same thing as the noun they follow.
Example: We had my favorite dessert, **chocolate cake**.

In each of the following sentences, underline the appositive and circle the noun it explains.
1. The uniform of George Martlin, the quarterback, was caked with mud.
2. The trophy, a tall bronze statue, was given to the team captain.
3. Shelley returned the books to Mrs. Hartzfeld, the new librarian.
4. The tour bus stopped at Mt. Vernon, the home of George Washington.
5. The hound, a mean-looking beast, bounded after the deer.
6. We went on vacation with Kim Ling and Su Yung, our cousins.
7. Karate, a martial art, requires a lot of mental discipline.
8. The judge asked to see Mr. Dwyer, the lawyer on the case.
9. We just met the Wileys, our nextdoor neighbors.
10. His burial site, an ancient mausoleum, has been restored.

Make the following subjects into complete sentences by writing an appositive and a predicate for each one.
1. The crew _____
2. The house _____
3. A bird _____
4. The song _____
5. A large leaf _____
6. Louise _____
7. The skaters _____
8. Dr. Leo _____
9. The score _____
10. Wayne _____

Choose an appropriate appositive from the right column and write it on the line next to a noun in the left column.

1. Marie, _____	the author
2. The rose, _____	John's wife
3. My name, _____	a competent woman
4. James Howard, _____	a graduate of Harvard
5. Their house, _____	a pink species
6. The director, _____	known as Sparky
7. The professor, _____	Veronica Birney
8. Rev. Smith, _____	the tax assessor
9. The head nurse, _____	a fine speaker
10. The dalmation, _____	the town's landmark

On a separate paper, rewrite the following story about the Vikings. Add an appropriate appositive where there is an asterisk (*).

The Vikings, sea rovers from Scandinavia, loved war and fighting. Their ships * carried raiding parties to many lands. The Runic alphabet * was used by the Vikings. Some of the Vikings explored and settled Greenland *. Most people were frightened when they heard of the approach of the Vikings. Before they set out on voyages, the men planted crops *. Grain * was harvested on their return. In the winter, the raiders prepared for the next trip. Games and entertainment * helped pass the long cold evenings.

A **pronoun** is a word used in place of a noun.

Example: **Connie** opened the book and began to read the **book**.

She opened the book and began to read **it**.

In the following paragraph, underline the nouns that could be replaced by pronouns to improve the sentences.

Leonardo da Vinci was one of Italy's finest artists. Leonardo painted a very famous picture of a woman. The woman is known as Mona Lisa. People have studied Mona Lisa's face for years. Still there is a puzzle about Mona Lisa. Who was Mona Lisa? Is Mona Lisa really smiling in the picture? Why? Only Leonardo could answer all of these questions. As far as we know, Leonardo never did.

Replace the nouns in boldfaced type with appropriate pronouns.

Example: **Michael** mixed two colors of paint together.

He mixed two colors of paint together.

1. Good lighting is important to **artists**. _____
2. The **easel** stood in a corner. _____
3. **Saul and Tina** are learning how to draw. _____
4. Do you like this **painting**? _____
5. **Patty** just bought a silver frame. _____
6. Sam carefully cleaned the **brushes**. _____
7. The judge gave the first prize to **Juan**. _____

The **antecedent** is the noun that is replaced by a pronoun.

Example: **Jill** followed the tour guide. **She** followed the tour guide. The antecedent is Jill.

At the end of the following paragraph, list the antecedent for each pronoun.

The largest amphitheater in ancient Rome was the Colosseum. **It** was four stories high and could hold almost 50,000 spectators. **They** sat on benches and watched the chariot races. **They** were very exciting because the horses and gladiators took the curves at such high speeds. The gladiators also fought wild lions. **They** were kept in cages below the wooden floor of the Colosseum. Hand-made machines pulled **them** up to floor level. When the gates were opened, the roaring lions charged at the gladiators.

It _____ They _____ They _____ They _____ them _____

Replace each of the nouns below with a pronoun. Then write a sentence using the pronoun.

Example: train—The whistle blew as **it** went into the tunnel.

1. actor _____
2. nurses _____
3. trapeze _____
4. vacation _____
5. Mrs. Palumbo _____
6. guitar _____
7. coach _____
8. Dr. Reed _____
9. crowd _____
10. Julia and Scott _____

EXTRA! Secretly choose a classmate. On a separate sheet of paper, write a few sentences describing your classmate using only pronouns. Do not write the person's name. After you have finished, trade papers with the person sitting next to you. See if he or she can guess the person you described in your sentences.

Harry's hints:
   A **pronoun** must refer clearly to its **antecedent**, a noun mentioned earlier in a sentence or paragraph.
Example: **The mall** was crowded on Saturday. **It** had many shoppers.
It refers to **the mall**.

Read the pairs of sentences below. Circle the pronoun in the second sentence and underline its antecedent in the first sentence.

1. John and Philip went to the hobby shop. They bought an airplane kit to assemble.
2. Beth bought a waffle ice cream cone. She loved the extra toppings.
3. The department store opened early for a sale. It was crowded.
4. Amy bought a blue sweatshirt. It was monogrammed with her name.
5. Cher and Elizabeth looked through books about horses. They love horses.
6. The mall was set up for School Week. It was a good celebration.
7. Mr. Palmer was asked to be in charge of the festival in the mall. Plans for it were started months ago.
8. Karen asked questions about the display of art from her school. It was to be exhibited for one week.
9. The gardens and fountains in the west wing were decorated. They looked especially festive for the occasion.
10. Several shops had special items for sale that would appeal to children of all ages. They were not expensive.

Do not use a pronoun and its antecedent together.
Example: My father **he** walks through the mall for exercise. (The pronoun **he** should be eliminated in this sentence. **He** can be used to refer to **father** in a sentence that follows.)

Cross out the pronouns that are not needed in the sentences.
1. The mall-walkers they often have their blood pressure checked.
2. The mall it is often crowded with early morning walkers.
3. My grandfather he loves to meet with friends as he walks.
4. John's aunt she walks before she leaves for her job.
5. Everyone they enjoys stopping later for a nice breakfast.

Use **I** in the subject part of a sentence. When it is used with another noun or pronoun, put **I** last. Use **me** in the predicate part of a sentence.
Examples: Carla and **I** bought a greeting card for Vern. Vern thanked her and **me**.

In the following sentences, circle the correct pronoun.
1. Harry and (me, I) walked all over the mall looking for a sturdy pair of running shoes.
2. Later in the afternoon we found my shoes after someone directed Harry and (I, me) to the right store.
3. He and (I, me) will try running later today so I can try my new shoes.
4. Susan told him and (I, me) about a new fitness course in the park.
5. My friends and (I, me) will sign up for the course.

Write a paragraph about yourself. Underline all pronouns in the paragraph.

A **pronoun** can be used as the **subject** of a sentence. **I**, **you**, **he**, **she**, **we**, **it**, and **they** are **personal pronouns** used as subjects.
Example: **I** traveled to Italy last summer.

In each sentence below, underline the correct pronoun in parentheses.
1. My uncle and (I, me) went to see the Leaning Tower of Pisa.
2. Are (they, them) really made of Venetian glass?
3. Why are the policemen and (he, him) waving their arms?
4. You and (she, her) must hurry back to the hotel.
5. Rosa and (you, me) will order sandwiches.
6. Did Beth and (us, we) stay here too?
7. Willa and (he, him) will be back soon.
8. (It, They) was the fastest way to travel in Europe.
9. Was it (I, me)?
10. Either Trina or (me, I) can help you.

A **pronoun** can be used as the **object** of a verb. **Me**, **you**, **him**, **her**, **us**, **it**, and **them** are **personal pronouns** used as objects.
Example: Uncle Tony took **me** to Italy.

In the blanks before each sentence, put a check mark if the pronoun is used correctly. If it is not, write the correct pronoun in the blank.
____ 1. Helen saw my brother and I at the shop.
____ 2. The shopkeeper's dog growled at them.
____ 3. Did you see they in the gondola?
____ 4. The boatman rowed us down the canals.
____ 5. The guide took Irving and me to the cathedral.
____ 6. Tomás gave he money for lunch.
____ 7. We cannot find George and them.
____ 8. I will meet she near the hotel.
____ 9. Vincent told me to join the others.
____ 10. Joel saved him from falling in the canal.

A **pronoun** can be used as the **object** of a preposition.
Example: The map was under **it**.

In the following sentences, fill in the blanks by substituting an object pronoun for the words in the left column.

Harold
Bill, June, Cynthia
Mario
Mrs. Hartstein
David
Arthur and Jerry
a man
the woman
Marshall
the tour

1. Pam wrote a letter to _____.
2. There were only five dollars among _____.
3. Sally sat between _____ and me.
4. The note was written by _____.
5. Will you be with _____ this afternoon?
6. Sue gave the menu to _____.
7. The policeman ran after _____.
8. The two came toward _____.
9. Chuck left the suitcases with _____.
10. We'll catch up with _____ tomorrow.

In the paragraph below, fill in the blanks with the correct pronoun as the subject, the object of a verb, or the object of a preposition.

Many newlyweds in Venice, Italy think a gondola ride will bring good luck to _____. _____ step aboard a boat and _____ glides down the Grand Canal. The boatman uses a large pole. _____ is very long and is used to push the boat along. The boat passes under many bridges. One of _____ is the famous Rialto Bridge. It is especially pretty at night when the lights are lit. _____ twinkle all along the banks of the canal. At the end of the ride, the couple thanks the boatman. It has been a pleasant ride for all of _____.

Harry's hint:
   Personal pronouns that replace nouns as the **subject** of a sentence are:
I, **you**, **he**, **she**, **we**, **it**, and **they**.
Example: **Sue** went to school quickly. **She** forgot her lunch.
   These pronouns are also used after forms of the verb **be**.
Example: The speaker was **Sue**. The speaker was **she**.
   Personal pronouns that replace nouns as the **objects** of a sentence are:
me, **you**, **him**, **her**, **us**, **it**, and **them**.
Example: John gave **Sue** an apple. John gave **her** an apple.
   These pronouns are also used after prepositions such as **to** or **for**.
Example: Sue gave the apple to **John**. Sue gave the apple to **him**.
   Notice that some pronouns can be both subject or object pronouns.

Circle the pronouns below. Write an **S** in the blank if the pronoun is used as a subject. Write an **O** if the pronoun is used as an object. (There may be more than one pronoun in a sentence.)

_____ 1. We were excited to be planning the 100th day celebration.

_____ 2. That is the day we will have been in school a total of 100 days.

_____ 3. Mrs. Perkins announced she would sponsor an essay contest.

_____ 4. All of us were eager to hear the details.

_____ 5. The contest was to write an essay about the most interesting project or lesson you had completed during our 100 days of school.

_____ 6. The class was asked to bring jars to her containing 100 objects of all types of items.

_____ 7. Susan and Caroline decided they would bring cereal in a baby bottle.

_____ 8. I was glad to participate in the collection of 100 items.

_____ 9. It was difficult, but most of us found unusual items to bring.

_____ 10. Several of us listed 100 new things we had learned in 100 days!

Replace the words in boldfaced type with the correct pronouns.

1. **Beth and Larry** collected lunch money in the morning. _____

2. **Jonathon** helped by opening the windows. _____

3. The teacher asked **Al and Tom** to write the agenda for the day. _____

4. The class planned a party for **James** who was moving to Ohio. _____

5. **The teacher** walked the class to the buses in front of school. _____

In the following pairs of sentences, underline the subject in the first sentence and replace it with the correct personal pronoun in the second sentence.

1. Miss Wilson started speaking. _____ called the class to attention as the fire bell sounded.

2. The class heard the first alarm. _____ moved quickly and quietly in a straight line for the door.

3. Edward was captain of the safety squad. _____ closed the door of the classroom as he left.

4. Mairin and Bethany were getting a drink at the water fountain. But _____ were able to join their class quickly in a line.

EXTRA!

Make a list of times when using only pronouns could be confusing to your reader. For example, would you use pronouns at the very beginning of a story? Why or why not? Give a reason for each answer.

A **singular pronoun** takes the place of a **singular noun**.
A **plural pronoun** takes the place of a **plural noun**.
Examples: Marvin bought **a book**. Marvin bought **it**. (singular)
         Margo bought **books**. Margo bought **them**. (plural)

In the blanks before each sentence, write an **S** if the pronoun used is singular, and a **P** if it is plural.

___ 1. We found the gloves on the bench.
___ 2. Carlos gave them to Jack.
___ 3. He did not want the gloves.
___ 4. They were far too large.

___ 5. "I will try on the gloves," said Gino.
___ 6. No, they did not fit.
___ 7. Mary and I took the gloves to the Lost and Found desk.

Write sentences using a pronoun for each of the following singular or plural nouns.
1. Marge and Ray _____
2. James _____
3. the firefighter _____
4. clowns _____
5. policewoman _____
6. buildings _____
7. Italy _____
8. sparrow _____
9. singers _____
10. gondola _____

A **possessive pronoun** takes the place of a possessive noun. Possessive pronouns that can be used before a noun are: **my**, **your**, **his**, **her**, **its**, **our**, and **their**.
Example: **My** invitation was lost.

Possessive pronouns that can be used alone are: **mine**, **yours**, **his**, **hers**, **its**, **ours**, and **theirs**.
Example: The invitation was **mine**.

In each of the following sentences, substitute a possessive pronoun for the possessive noun in parentheses.
1. The idea for the surprise party was (Larry's). _____
2. I put an invitation in (Theresa's) mailbox. _____
3. (Peg's) new camera was very expensive. _____
4. This watch is just like (Mr. Lerner's). _____
5. That Siamese cat is (the twins'). _____
6. Stephen borrowed (Tony's) flashlight. _____
7. (Angela's) coat is lined with fur. _____
8. The black purse is (the author's). _____
9. The last car in the parking lot is (Joe's). _____
10. No one could find (the driver's) keys. _____

EXTRA! Select a short paragraph from a book or story you have recently read. On another sheet of paper, make two lists: **personal pronouns** and **possessive pronouns**. Write down all of the pronouns from your paragraph on the correct list.

Harry's hints:
    Possessive pronouns show ownership. Do not use an apostrophe with a possessive pronoun.
    Possessive pronouns that can be used before a noun are: **my**, **your**, **his**, **her**, **its**, **our**, and **their**.
    Possessive pronouns that can be used alone are: **mine**, **yours**, **his**, **her**, **its**, **ours**, and **theirs**.

Examples:
My house is white.	The white house is **mine**.
Your house is blue.	The blue house is **yours**.
His house is cedar.	The cedar house is **his**.
Her house is brick.	The brick house is **hers**.
Its house is a birdhouse.	The birdhouse is **its**.
Our house is a two-story.	The two-story is **ours**.
Their house is nice.	The nice house is **theirs**.

Underline the correct form of pronoun for each sentence.
1. We are building birdhouses for (our, ours) class project.
2. (It, Its) theme is learning how to manage a small business.
3. Joanne is happy the president's job is (her, hers).
4. The job of painting the houses is (their, theirs).
5. The task of keeping business records belongs to (my, mine) friend.
6. We learned so much from (our, ours) marketing project.
7. (My, mine) job was to buy materials such as wood, nails, and paint.
8. (Our, ours) class voted on (their, theirs) idea of painting the houses red.
9. Susan thought the class would vote for (her, hers) idea.
10. The class agreed that the profits would be used for (their, theirs) year-end picnic.

Circle the possessive pronouns that come before nouns and underline the possessive pronouns that stand alone.
1. Mrs. Tabscot brought her paint brushes and I brought mine.
2. Jennifer offered to supply our class with newspapers.
3. We worked after school with his paint and my cut-wood pieces.
4. My friend offered to bring her saw and Anna and I offered to bring ours.
5. If I agreed to bring my supplies, everyone seemed agreeable to bringing theirs.

Change the words in boldfaced type to possessive pronouns. Then rewrite the sentences on the lines below.
1. **Mrs. Tabscot's** adding machine stopped working when Mrs. Tabscot accidentally pushed the "off" button.

_____

_____

2. Ricky and Melissa's mother came by with **Ricky and Melissa's** wagon, which was needed to carry the birdhouses to the market.

_____

_____

EXTRA! Write a journal entry about your favorite school project this year. Describe your role in the project, as well as the roles of your classmates. Underline all possessive pronouns in the entry.

Read the description of the **pronouns** in each section. In the four sentences following the description, find the pronouns of that type and write them on the lines. Underline all the pronouns in every section.

Personal pronouns are the most common type of pronouns.
1. We enjoyed the party very much.
2. Thank you for inviting us.
3. We followed her out of the subdivision.
4. She thought they were mine.

1. _____ 2. _____ 3. _____ 4. _____

Indefinite pronouns do not indicate a definite person, place, or thing.
5. Has someone told you about our group?
6. A few of us meet every week.
7. Something is always happening in that particular group of people.
8. After a few weeks you will know everyone.

5. _____ 6. _____ 7. _____ 8. _____

Demonstrative pronouns point out their antecedent emphatically.
9. These are the best years of your life.
10. Jan liked this more than that, didn't she?
11. Those are the kind I prefer.
12. Didn't you take that too seriously?

9. _____ 10. _____ 11. _____ 12. _____

Reflexive pronouns reflect back to nouns or pronouns used earlier in the sentence. They cannot be omitted from the sentence without changing the meaning of the sentence.
13. It will wear itself out eventually.
14. You should see yourselves on the videotape.
15. Sometimes I, myself, see you talking to yourself.
16. Your self-image is important.

13. _____ 14. _____ 15. _____ 16. _____

Interrogative pronouns ask a question.
17. With those qualifications to consider, who else would I choose?
18. What are you talking about?
19. Which would you select?
20. With whom have you been speaking?

17. _____ 18. _____ 19. _____ 20. _____

Relative pronouns relate a group of words to a preceding noun or pronoun.
21. These are people who are very lonely.
22. The dog, which I saw on the road, was hers.
23. I enjoyed the cake, which was made for my birthday.
24. A boy, whose name I won't mention, is quite handsome.

21. _____ 22. _____ 23. _____ 24. _____

Possessive pronouns are personal pronouns that show ownership or possession.
25. The airline lost our luggage.
26. Do you have yours?
27. My brother lost his passport recently.
28. The dog lost its tag, but it's going to be taken anyway.

25. _____ 26. _____ 27. _____ 28. _____

Name _____ Date _____

HARRY'S PUZZLING PRONOUNS

Write the answers in the puzzle. Use the words in the Word Box.

ACROSS
2. The boy admitted the toy was ____.
5. Pronoun used for showing ownership.
7. Possessive pronouns show ____.
12. Do not confuse some possessive pronouns with ____.
13. ____ and I may go to the movies.
14. ____ and I will organize a Fun Fair.
15. ____ told me to rescue the cat in the tree.
17. The teacher told ____ to stop talking.
18. ____ sweater was beautifully knitted.
19. I appreciate my math teacher and I like ____.
20. Form of pronoun used after action words and prepositions.
21. This afghan is his and that one is ____.

DOWN
1. The computer disk belongs to me; it is ____.
2. They hooked up the video recorder to ____ television.
3. The electrician helped ____ with our science experiment.
4. The punctuation mark needed in a contraction.
5. The pronoun used after a linking verb is called a ____ pronoun.
6. We enthusiastically prepared for our medieval festival. We loved ____.
8. Subject pronoun for boy.
9. A predicate pronoun follows a ____. (two words)
10. The award was presented to ____. (object pronoun for boy)
11. Object pronoun for a group of people other than yourself.
14. Type of pronoun used as a subject of a sentence.
16. It was ____ basketball that we found.
20. We discovered that it was ____ mistake.

WORD BOX
APOSTROPHE
CONTRACTIONS
HE
HER
HERS
HIM
IT
LINKING VERB
ME
MINE
OBJECT
OUR
OURS
OWNERSHIP
POSSESSIVE
PREDICATE
SHE
SUBJECT
THEIR
THEIRS
THEM
THEY
US
WE
YOU
YOUR
YOURS

Name _____ Date _____

Determiners are words that **point to** or **help determine nouns.**
Indefinite determiners are **a** and **an.** (**A** and **an** are also called **articles.**) **Definite determiners** are **adjectives, demonstrative adjectives,** or **possessive pronouns** used as adjectives.
Examples: **a** house, **the** house, **one** house, **that** house, and **her** house.

Write the **indefinite article a** or **an** in front of each noun below. Use **a** when the noun begins with a consonant sound or the sound of long u. Use **an** when the noun begins with a vowel sound.

1. ___ astronaut   5. ___ igloo   9. ___ accident   13. ___ umbrella
2. ___ home   6. ___ tree   10. ___ voice   14. ___ roof
3. ___ automobile   7. ___ orange   11. ___ table   15. ___ unicorn
4. ___ clock   8. ___ glass   12. ___ storm

On the lines below, write an **I** if there is an indefinite determiner in the sentence and a **D** if there is a definite one.

___ 1. Madrid is a city in Spain.
___ 2. Popular Spanish dances include the "bolero."
___ 3. The Spanish olives grow in warm areas.
___ 4. Isabella was a queen.
___ 5. Many of the Spanish people are farmers.
___ 6. Christopher Columbus received a gift of money from Isabella.
___ 7. With it, he made the voyage to discover America.
___ 8. Another Spanish explorer discovered the Mississippi River.
___ 9. St. Louis was under the rule of Spain for many years.
___ 10. The Spanish influence in America is still strong.

Underline the **numeral determiners** in the sentences below.
1. There were three ships in Columbus' first fleet.
2. Five men fell overboard.
3. The fourth tin box of flour was damp.
4. One star shone brighter than the rest.
5. The captain's log had more than fifty entries.
6. They celebrated their twentieth day at sea.
7. The first spoonful of soup was too hot.
8. Four sails tore in the sea wind.
9. Sailors rolled two barrels of tar across the deck.

Fill in the blanks below with the determiners **this** or **these** before nouns that would be close by in a normal classroom. Put an **X** in front of those nouns that are far away from the classroom.

1. _____ chalkboard   5. _____ airport   9. _____ gymnasium
2. _____ yacht   6. _____ arithmetic problems 10. _____ ice rink
3. _____ stack of books 7. _____ closet   11. _____ lunchboxes
4. _____ windowsills   8. _____ islands   12. _____ dog

Use one of the following **possessive determiners** in the blanks below: **my, our, your, his, her, its,** or **their.**

1. _____ horse was difficult for him to control.
2. We gave _____ tickets to the bus driver.
3. The piano is _____ favorite instrument.
4. Mrs. Tyson is _____ principal.
5. The robin bruised _____ wing.
6. _____ dress fits perfectly.

7. William fixed _____ bicycle in one afternoon.
8. We had to clean snow off _____ sidewalks.
9. Stanley put the money in _____ pocket.
10. The road crew fixed the street in front of _____ apartment.

Name _____   Date _____

Prefix	Meaning	Example	
re	again	write	rewrite
over	extra, more	achieve	overachieve
pre	before	view	preview
co	with	exist	coexist
mis	wrongly	interpret	misinterpret
un	opposite of	kind	unkind

Underline the word that has a prefix in each sentence. Define the meaning of that word.

1. The students untightened their skates. _____

2. John misunderstood what time the class started. _____

3. The instructor repeated the lesson several times. _____

4. They all cooperated with the captain of the skating team. _____

5. They unlocked their lockers to put away tennis shoes. _____

Suffix	Meaning	Example	
ful	full of	hope	hopeful
less	without	pain	painless
ish	like	pink	pinkish
able	can be	return	returnable
er	one who	teach	teacher

Add the suffixes above to the root words below to make six new words. Write the new words and their meanings.

spell   joy   play   mix   fool   color

New word   Meaning

1. _____

2. _____

3. _____

4. _____

5. _____

6. _____

P.S. from Harry:
     Do you drink **soda** or **pop**? Do you sit on a **davenport** or a **couch**? These English language words vary from region to region and from England to the United States. How many differences do you know? Draw a line between the words and phrases that mean the same thing.

U.S. Words	English Phrases	Regional Words	
elevator	petrol	cellar	submarine
policeman	boot of a car	sack	chimney
gasoline	lift	hero	poke
trunk	bobby	flue	basement

Name _____ Date _____

The **root or base** is the part of a word to which a **prefix** or a **suffix**, or both, is attached. Knowing more about the **roots** or **bases** of words will be helpful in building a better vocabulary.

The root **pend** is from a Latin word and means **hang**.

Write a definition of each of the following words that are rooted or based on **pend**. Use a dictionary to help.

1. depend _____
2. pendant _____
3. pending _____
4. pendulum _____
5. suspend _____
6. suspense _____

Choose three of the above words and use each one in a sentence that clearly shows the meaning of the root **pend**.

1. _____
2. _____
3. _____

A **prefix** is one or more syllables added **before the root** that can change the word's meaning.
A **suffix** is one or more syllables added **after the root** that can change the word's meaning.

Example: re   place   ment
           (prefix)   (root)   (suffix)

Write three words starting with each of the following prefixes. Then use one of the new words in a sentence.

1. trans (across) _____   _____   _____

   _____

2. anti (against) _____   _____   _____

3. mono (one) _____   _____   _____

   _____

4. un (not) _____   _____   _____

5. port (carry) _____   _____   _____

   _____

Underline the **suffix** in each of the following words. Circle the roots.

1. firmness   2. appearance   3. really   4. pavement   5. beginning

Try to build as many additional words as possible from the following list of roots. There are at least two more possible for each.
Some other helpful prefixes: **pro**, **dis**, **re**.
Some other helpful suffixes: **ed**, **ness**, **less**, **ly**.

frost _____   _____   appear _____   _____
color _____   _____   want _____   _____
collect _____   _____   count _____   _____
port _____   _____   last _____   _____
press _____   _____   firm _____   _____

EXTRA! Create as many new words as possible by adding prefixes and suffixes to the root **do**. Use a dictionary to help you.

Harry's hint:
A **contraction** is a word or words made up of two words combined into one by leaving out one or more letters.
A contraction is usually used in informal conversation, not in formal letters or writing.

I ♡ Short-cuts!

Use an **apostrophe** (') to show where the letter or letters are missing in the contractions below.

is not	isn t	could not	couldn t	should not	shouldn t
are not	aren t	would not	wouldn t	must not	mustn t
was not	wasn t	will not	won t	were not	weren t
has not	hasn t	have not	haven t	does not	doesn t
do not	don t	cannot	can t	you are	you re
they are	they re	she will	she ll	you will	you ll
I will	I ll	I am	I m	I have	I ve
he is	he s	she is	she s	that is	that s

Write four sentences, using a contraction from above in each one.

1. _____
2. _____
3. _____
4. _____

Spell the contraction for the words below and put it in the puzzle. The word spelled will help you remember what you are learning.

1. could not   C O U L D N ' T
2. will not
3. was not
4. have not
5. were not
6. are not
7. cannot
8. do not
9. is not
10. does not
11. should not

Sometimes contractions are confused with possessive pronouns. It's, they're, and you're are contractions. Its, their, and your are possessive pronouns, showing ownership. They do not have an apostrophe.

Underline the contraction or the possessive pronoun in each parentheses to make the sentence correct.

1. (Its, It's) a very warm day today.
2. (Their, They're) house sold quickly.
3. I love (you're, your) flowers in the front yard.
4. (They're, Their) so colorful this time of the year.
5. (Your, You're) sad that you are selling your house.
6. (It's, Its) beautiful yard will help it to sell.

Harry's hints:
    A **contraction** is a shortened form of two words. An **apostrophe** is used to show where one or more letters have been left out.
    A contraction can be made of a **verb** and **not**.
Examples: did not—didn't, are not—aren't
    A contraction can be made of a **pronoun** and a **verb**.
Examples: she has—she's, they are—they're

Write the pronoun and the verb that creates each contraction:

she's _____   I'm _____   you've _____

it's _____   they'd _____   I'll _____

Write the contraction for each pronoun and verb:

I have _____   they will _____   it has _____

he is _____   you are _____   we had _____

In the Word Find below, circle pairs of words that will form a contraction. Write the contraction of the words on the lines at the right.

WORD FIND

```
I  F  V  T  J  Q  T  P  H  I  R  M  Q  W  X
Y  O  U  H  A  V  E  H  S  W  E  H  A  D  P
H  E  J  T  Z  B  M  A  Y  I  H  E  H  A  S
E  D  U  Y  O  U  W  I  L  L  X  I  E  F  O
H  C  S  R  L  A  K  T  C  L  I  S  O  N  Y
A  I  H  A  V  E  B  I  L  N  A  M  Z  F  D
D  K  V  X  B  C  D  S  H  E  W  I  L  L  G
```

1. _____   6. _____
2. _____   7. _____
3. _____   8. _____
4. _____   9. _____
5. _____   10. _____

In the following paragraph, circle the contractions. On the blanks following the paragraph, write the pronoun and the verb each contraction represents.

We're planning a camping trip to the Colorado Rockies this spring. We think it's a great experience to sleep in tents under the beautiful sky. Our leader taught us what we'll need to know to survive in the wilderness. She's explained how to use a knife and build a campfire. It'll be very exciting. We've heard about the great adventure of riding the rapids in a raft.

_____   _____   _____   _____   _____   _____

Write five sentences about an adventure that you have had or would like to have someday. Choose five of the following contractions and use one correctly in each sentence.

        I'll   he'd   she'll   we'd   it's   they're   you'll

1. _____
2. _____
3. _____
4. _____
5. _____

Sometimes possessive pronouns are confused with contractions. Possessive pronouns **do not** have apostrophes. In the sentences below, circle the correct possessive pronoun or contraction.

1. (It's, Its) time to put up the tent.
2. What sturdy fabric (it's, its) made from!
3. Please give me (it's, its) stakes.

4. (You're, your) really a big help.
5. I think we have room for (you're, your) sleeping bag.

Harry's hint:
    A **verb** is the main word in the **predicate**
of the sentence. It can be an **action word**
telling what the subject does or did.

lights, camera ACTION!

Underline the action verb in each sentence.

1. Our class studied dinosaurs last spring.
2. Dinosaurs are known to have had very small brains.
3. The age of dinosaurs started about 200 million years ago.
4. Some dinosaurs ate the plants found in great quantities.
5. The dinosaurs dominated the earth for millions of years.
6. Flesh-eating dinosaurs preyed upon the plant-eating dinosaurs.
7. Stegosaurs were protected by upright bony plates on their backs.
8. Some dinosaurs lived in swamps with other types of animals.
9. Scientists have learned about dinosaurs by studying fossils.
10. Dinosaurs fought with different types of dinosaurs.

        Sometimes a noun follows the verb and receives the action of the verb. It is called a
direct object.

Underline the action verb and circle the direct object.

1. We discovered interesting facts about dinosaurs.

2. Dinosaurs laid eggs on land.

3. Paleontologists study fossils.

4. Scientists have learned many reasons why dinosaurs died.

5. The formation of mountain ranges caused the seaways to be drained.

    Using exact verbs makes for clearer understanding by the reader. Using the verbs below, write
sentences about a trip to a science museum to study dinosaurs.

        scolded   scurried   smiled   watched   frightened

1. _____

   _____

2. _____

   _____

3. _____

   _____

4. _____

   _____

5. _____

   _____

The **predicate** part of a sentence tells about the subject. It contains a **verb**.

Write three sentences in which the predicate tells what the subject **is, was, or will be doing**.
Example: The twins **will swim in the first meet of the year**.

1. _____
2. _____
3. _____

Write three sentences in which the predicate tells what the subject **is, was, or will be**.
Example: Ms. Hartsfield **is our teacher**.

4. _____
5. _____
6. _____

Write three sentences in which the predicate **describes** the subject.
Example: The gorilla **was large and hairy**.

7. _____
8. _____
9. _____

Write three sentences in which the predicate tells **what happened** to the subject.
Example: Rachel's car **was hit by a truck**.

10. _____
11. _____
12. _____

The **verb** is the main part of the **predicate**.
Example: Dinosaurs **lived** long ago.

Circle the verb in each of the following sentences.

1. They ate hamburgers for lunch.
2. Sherman swept the kitchen floor.
3. Please give me an apple.
4. Astronauts do not always sit upright.
5. The cabin stands near the road.
6. A picket fence surrounds the yard.
7. Many visitors swim in the cold stream.
8. Duk Soo hit a home run.
9. Jackie climbed the rope.
10. The raccoon scampered up the old oak tree.
11. Cautiously, Vernon peered around the corner.
12. The baby clapped his hands in delight at the sight of the clown.

The verb with all its modifiers and complements is a **complete predicate**.
Write an appropriate subject for the following complete predicates.

1. _____ chewed happily on a bone.
2. _____ leaped high into the air.
3. _____ blew the papers all over the yard.
4. _____ will stay at an expensive hotel.
5. _____ found her watch on the shelf.
6. _____ shut the door quietly.
7. _____ rode over the bridge and into town.
8. _____ will spend the weekend with his aunt.

EXTRA!

Write three different complete predicates for the following subject:
The brand new bicycle

A **verb** is a word that expresses **action** or a **state of being**.

Circle the words that could be used as verbs.

was	detective	imagine	lighten	material	brightly	remain	stimulus
good	seize	tightly	looks	appear	region	work	became

Selecting the right verb makes writing more descriptive. Give two verbs that could be used to replace the plain verb which has been used. Underline the verb being replaced.

1. I walk to school every day.   _____ _____

2. I talk to my friends at lunch.   _____ _____

3. We eat our food.   _____ _____

4. The teacher gives us homework.   _____ _____

5. I yell at my friends outdoors.   _____ _____

In the following sentences, underline action verbs with one line and verbs of being with two lines. Some sentences have more than one verb.

1. The *Titanic* sailed out of the Southhampton harbor on Wednesday, April 10, 1912.
2. This ship was the largest and most luxurious vessel on the seas.
3. An orchestra played as the passengers danced on a veranda.
4. The builders equipped the *Titanic* with the Marconi Telegraph, a state–of–the–art radio.
5. Some passengers worried for their safety on this massive boat.
6. The captain assured everyone that the ship was unsinkable.
7. The *Titanic* glided through the night of April 14, even though a message warned her captain that icebergs were in the area.
8. An iceberg appeared directly in front of the ship.
9. The *Titanic* collided with the iceberg, but the passengers were oblivious to the danger.
10. Snow and ice covered the prow.
11. The captain inspected the damage and called for the lifeboats.
12. There was an ominous lack of panic on the sinking ship.
13. While the band played, women and children boarded lifeboats.
14. A sense of urgency developed when the boat began to tilt upward.
15. The remaining passengers scrambled to get into the lifeboats, but there was no room.
16. Less than three hours after it hit the iceberg, the *Titanic* dove toward the ocean floor.
17. Passengers and crew leaped into the sea.
18. Survivors became heroes.
19. People saw their loved ones die in the frigid sea.
20. Help arrived two hours later, but only 705 people survived.
21. The worst disaster at sea claimed the lives of 1,517 people.

Harry's hint:
An **action verb** can be one word or it may be used with a **helping verb** such as: **am**, **is**, **are**, **was**, **were**, **have**, **has**, and **had**.
Examples: The boy **sanded** the model car. (**Sanded** is the action verb.)
The boy **has sanded** the model car. (**Has** is the helping verb and **sanded** is the main verb.)

Underline the helping verb once and the main verb twice.

1. Henry Ford was known to be a creative industrialist.
2. He had developed an affordable automobile.
3. The Model T automobile was sold at a reasonable price.
4. The assembly line was created to keep costs down.
5. Henry Ford had made the decision to use his profits to increase the size of his factories.
6. He changed the way workers were treated by companies.
7. He was opposed in that decision by many stockholders.
8. Later he had decided to buy out the other stockholders.
9. In his later years, he had established Greenfield Village in Dearborn, Michigan.
10. He had moved many exhibits there to show man's progress in modernization of our lives.

In the following sentences, some of the verbs have helping verbs and some do not. If a sentence has a helping verb, write **HV** in the blank.

_____ 1. My family visited Greenfield Village and saw the exhibit of Thomas Edison's laboratory.
_____ 2. We were visiting several different styles of homes built in the early days of our country.
_____ 3. We were watching several craftsmen make different items popular during the early 1800s.
_____ 4. My father was walking near an old-fashioned windmill.
_____ 5. We saw a memorial to Stephen Foster, an American composer.
_____ 6. The landmarks are restored to their natural quality.
_____ 7. My sister enjoyed the ride on the authentic riverboat.
_____ 8. The Henry Ford Museum was located nearby.
_____ 9. The building where we were visiting was enormous.
_____ 10. The museum had collected fascinating exhibits about transportation.

Write five sentences about a trip you have taken or would like to take. Use one helping verb and main verb in each sentence.

1. _____
_____
2. _____
_____
3. _____
_____
4. _____
_____
5. _____
_____

Name _____   Date _____

Harry's hint:
A **linking verb** joins the subject to a word in the predicate. A linking verb **renames** or **describes** the subject.
Examples: The teacher **is** a man. He **seems** very nice.
There are two kinds of linking verbs. One kind uses forms of the verb **be**: **am**, **is**, **are**, **was**, and **were**.
Examples: The classroom **was** empty. The windows **were** open.
The other kind of linking verb uses verbs of the **senses**:
look, **appear**, **seem**, **feel**, **smell**, and **sound**.
Examples: The substitute teacher **appears** nervous.
The class **seems** anxious to meet him.

linking verb

In the following sentences, underline the linking verbs. Identify the verbs as either verbs of being or verbs of the senses by writing **Being** or **Senses** on the lines.

_____   1. Our class is about to begin rehearsal of our spring play.
_____   2. We were glad to do a comedy.
_____   3. Our teacher was the director.
_____   4. He seemed happy to be working with us.
_____   5. Joanna is the main character in the play.
_____   6. I appeared calm, but I was afraid to be on stage.
_____   7. Ricardo was the grandfather in the first act.
_____   8. The first rehearsal was fun.
_____   9. Susannah seemed jealous of Joanna at first.
_____ 10. She feels better about her role now.

Using the following subjects, write five sentences using verbs of being as linking verbs. The words below can be used to rename or describe the subjects.

| prompter | cautious | happy | excellent | brother | heavy |
| volunteer | nervous | quiet | talented | relaxed | nervous |

1. My mother _____.
2. The audience _____.
3. The cast _____.
4. The piano player _____.
5. The stage curtain _____.

Using the following subjects, write five sentences using the verbs of the senses as linking verbs. The words below can be used to rename or describe the subjects.

wonderful   teacher   busy   nervous   fun   work   creative
1. The director _____.
2. The stage manager _____.
3. Intermission _____.
4. Rehearsal _____.
5. The cast party _____.

Name _____ Date _____

Harry's hints:
    An **irregular verb** does not add **ed** to show the past tense. **Most** irregular verbs change form in the past and the past participle.
Examples: I **wear** a new dress.   present
              I **wore** a new dress.   past
              I **have worn** a new dress.   past participle
    Some irregular verbs have the same form in the past and the past participle.
Examples: We **bring** the box home.   present
              We **brought** the box home.   past
              We **have brought** the box home.   past participle
    There is no specific rule for changing forms in irregular verbs. The forms must be learned. A dictionary may be used to find the entry for the present tense of the verb, which will indicate the past forms.

Complete the following chart using the correct forms of these irregular verbs:

Present, plural, you or I	Present, singular	Present Participle, with form of be	Past	Past Participle, with form of have	Future, with will
1. wear					
2. steal					
3. know					
4. see					
5. eat					
6. drive					
7. sing					
8. freeze					
9. ring					
10. go					
11. write					
12. say					
13. think					
14. swim					
15. tear					
16. take					
17. fly					
18. choose					
19. grow					
20. ride					

In the following sentences, underline the irregular verbs. In the space at the left, identify the tense as: Present, Present Participle, Past, Past Participle, or Future.
_____ 1. We see the circus clowns performing.
_____ 2. I always have thought clowns were funny.
_____ 3. The tiny clown with the umbrella will ride on an elephant.
_____ 4. He is stealing the show!
_____ 5. I knew you would love the clowns.

Name _____   Date _____

Harry's hints:
Verbs in the **present tense** show action that is happening **now**.

With **plural** subjects, or **you**, or **I**, do not add **s** or **es** to the verb.
The boys **swim** the backstroke.
I **swim** the butterfly stroke.
You **time** the first race.

With **singular** subjects:
add **s** to most verbs.
Joan **swims** the crawl.
add **es** to verbs that end with sh, ch, x, s or z.
She **watches** the race.
change **y** to **i** and add **es** if a verb ends with a consonant and y.
Jo **studies** their form.

Write the correct present tense form for the verbs in parentheses.
(cheer)   1. The spectators _____ for their school team.
(dive)   2. The girl _____ for Kennedy High School.
(swim)   3. You _____ in the youth division of the meet.
(know)   4. Betty and John _____ they are fastest in their race.
(watch)   5. My mother _____ me during each race.
(study)   6. Our coach _____ each team member closely.
(practice)   7. I _____ every morning at 5:30 before school.
(hurry)   8. Marian _____ from the shower room to the pool.
(buzz)   9. The warning alarm to start the race _____.
(talk)   10. The coach _____ to the whole team to build morale before the meet.

Write an **S** in the blank if the subject of the sentence is **singular**. Write a **P** if it is **plural**. In the parentheses, circle the correct form of the present tense verbs.
____ 1. The meet (begin, begins) soon.
____ 2. I (wish, wishes) that I had practiced a little harder.
____ 3. The crowd (cheer, cheers) loudly at the end of each race.
____ 4. My mom (volunteers, volunteer) to be a timer.
____ 5. Judges (try, tries) to be fair while watching divers.
____ 6. Platform diving (look, looks) difficult.
____ 7. Anna (prepares, prepare) herself mentally by thinking through her dive first.
____ 8. My little sister (fuss, fusses) by the end of the long meet.
____ 9. The team (cheer, cheers) for all our teammates.
____ 10. The fruit juice and cookies (taste, tastes) delicious after the meet.

Rewrite each sentence below. Change the singular subjects to plural subjects and change the plural subjects to singular subjects. Change the verbs to agree with the subjects.

1. The young girl swims for Sugar Tree Swim Club. _____

_____

2. The diving coaches discipline the squad with early morning practices. _____

_____

3. The flag flies briskly over the finish line. _____

_____

EXTRA!
Write two sentences about something that is happening now. Use verbs in the present tense. Label your subjects as singular or plural.

Harry's hint:
   Verbs in the **past tense** show action that happened **before** now. They are used with both **singular** and **plural** subjects.
                    Rules for Making the Past Tense of Regular Verbs
   1. Add **ed** to form the **past tense** of most **regular verbs**.
Example: Susan **helped** put on a roof for the older couple.
   2. When a verb ends in **e**, drop the **e** and add **ed**.
Example: We **stared** at our handy work.
   3. When the verb ends with a consonant and **y**, change the **y** to **i** and add **ed**.
Example: Sam **worried** he wouldn't know how to use a sabre saw.
   4. When a verb has one vowel and ends with a single consonant, double the final consonant and add **ed**. There are some exceptions.
Examples: Harold **grabbed** a hammer. He **fixed** the door.

Past Tense

Write the past tense of each verb. Write the number of the rule used to determine the spelling.

1. like   _____ __   6. hurry   _____ __
2. scrub   _____ __   7. handle   _____ __
3. destroy   _____ __   8. swap   _____ __
4. study   _____ __   9. talk   _____ __
5. zip   _____ __   10. marry   _____ __

Write the past tense of each regular verb below the correct heading.

bury	chase	explode	bloom	rest	laugh	hope
carry	line	dash	pass	hurry	reply	tie
tidy	worry	bake	cry	admire	spell	marry
stare	apply	grab	slip	tap	bat	scrub

Add **ed**	Drop **e**; add **ed**	Change **y** to **i**; add **ed**	One vowel and single consonant; double consonant, add **ed**
_____	_____	_____	
_____	_____	_____	_____
_____	_____	_____	_____
_____	_____	_____	_____
_____	_____	_____	_____
_____	_____	_____	
	_____	_____	
	_____		

Write three sentences using three of the following verbs rewritten in the past tense: believe, study, stop, open, hurry, zip, bungle, cry.

1. _____
   _____
2. _____
   _____
3. _____
   _____

Harry's hint:
    The **future tense** of a verb shows action that **will happen** in the future. It is formed by using the helping verb **will** with a **main verb**.
Examples: She **helps** the children now. (present tense)
            She **will help** the children with their homework next week. (future tense)

Future!

In the following sentences, underline the verbs used in the future tense.

1. The 21st century will bring many changes to our lives.
2. People will use computers for many more projects than presently.
3. Travelers will have vacations planned by computer.
4. We will shop by phone or computer.
5. Some people will work at home with a computer.

In the following sentences, underline the verb. Then write the future tense of that verb on the line.

1. We study many things through the computer. _____
2. Our computer class programs music through our computer. _____
3. We type our essays on the word processor. _____
4. We have an electronic mailroom on the computer. _____
5. The class corresponds to different classmates through the computer. _____
6. We also learn the correct typing positions for our fingers. _____
7. One class operates a video program on a weekly basis. _____
8. The video news appears in the hallway to keep us up-to-date on school activities. _____
9. The fifth-grade publishes a monthly newspaper on the computer. _____
10. The editorial staff edits the first drafts written by reporters. _____

Time is measured by minutes, hours, days, and years. In grammar, the present, present participle, past, past participle, and future tenses are used to express time. In the following sentences, identify the verb tenses.

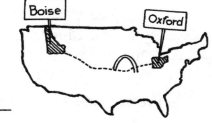

1. My family is planning to move to Idaho. _____
2. We have lived in Oxford, Ohio, for ten years. _____
3. Our neighbors in Ohio are wonderful to us. _____
4. I will hate to leave. _____
5. My dad's new business is locating outside Boise. _____
6. We sold our house in two weeks. _____
7. We held a garage sale in the driveway last Saturday. _____
8. My mother packed all last week. _____
9. The movers are taking all the boxes from the living room. _____
10. We cleaned carefully after the moving van left for Idaho. _____
11. Our neighbors gave us a bag of snacks to eat in the car. _____
12. The automobile trip across the Midwest was planned carefully. _____

Look at a map or globe. Write the names of several states that you would pass through while driving from Ohio to Idaho. Write a short paragraph about your trip using the future tense of different verbs.

Harry's hints:

The **present participle** is a verb tense formed by adding **ing** to a regular verb. A form of **be** serves as a helping verb before the present participle. This tense is used when the action is continuing over a period of time.

Examples: I **am studying** the stars with my telescope.

He **is watching** the moon.

We **were following** the movement of the stars.

The **past participle** is a verb tense formed by adding **ed** to a regular verb. A form of **have** serves as a helping verb. When **have** or **has** is used, the past participle describes action that has happened recently. When **had** is used, the past participle refers to something that ended before other events took place.

Examples: I **had purchased** a telescope last summer.

Saul **has helped** me move it to the roof.

We **have focused** it carefully.

PRESENT PARTICIPLE   PAST PARTICIPLE

In the sentences below, fill in the blanks with the correct helping verb in the parentheses. Then write **Present** if the present participle was completed, or **Past** if the past participle was completed.

_____ 1. The astronomer _____ speaking to our science class today. (was, had)

_____ 2. We _____ expected a boring speech, but she surprised us. (had, were)

_____ 3. The audience _____ sitting quietly as she began. (was, had)

_____ 4. The movie screen _____ moving into place as we sit down. (is, has)

_____ 5. The slide show _____ explored the limits of the solar system. (was, had)

_____ 6. Stars _____ shining from hot gases. (are, had)

_____ 7. Planets _____ reflecting the light from the sun. (has, are)

_____ 8. The planets _____ changed their positions in relation to the stars. (have, are)

_____ 9. The Greeks _____ noted the movement of the stars. (were, had)

_____ 10. By the end of the lecture, we _____ learned so much about the solar system. (were, had)

Write five sentences using the present participle of the following verbs:

move   talk   sit   play   shout

1. _____

2. _____

3. _____

4. _____

5. _____

Write five sentences using the past participle of the following verbs:

cheer   start   chase   call   protest

1. _____

2. _____

3. _____

4. _____

5. _____

Name _____ Date _____

Write the **past, past participle,** and **present participle** for each **regular verb**. Then rewrite each sentence, changing the verb to the tense shown in parentheses.

1. bake _____   _____   _____
   We bake the cake in a moderate oven.

   (past) _____

   present participle) _____

2. wave _____   _____   _____
   Children wave to their parents.

   (present participle) _____

   (past) _____

3. march _____   _____   _____
   The band members march down the street.

   (past participle) _____

   (present participle) _____

4. paint _____   _____   _____
   The artists paint with oils on canvas.

   (past) _____

   (present participle) _____

Write the **past, past participle,** and **present participle** for each **irregular verb**. Then rewrite each sentence, changing the verb to the tense shown in parentheses.

1. ring _____   _____   _____
   Tina and her friends ring the doorbell.

   (past) _____

   (past participle) _____

2. lead _____   _____   _____
   Some people lead fascinating lives.

   (present participle) _____

   (past participle) _____

3. go _____   _____   _____
   Picnickers go to the park across town.

   (past participle) _____

   (past) _____

Underline the verb in each sentence. On the line, identify the verb tense as present, present participle, past, or past participle.

1. The tailback immediately sprang into action. _____
2. Wendy is bursting to tell us the secret. _____
3. They have traveled across the United States many times. _____
4. Has Cheryl caught as many fish as you? _____
5. I wrapped a very nice present for my best friend. _____
6. The infant is crying. _____
7. Kevin has often waded in the frigid waters of Alaska. _____
8. Is the moon rising tonight at exactly 9:32? _____
9. Katherine rang the bell at the correct intervals. _____
10. Some varieties of snakes strike without warning. _____

Name _____   Date _____

Harry's hint:
    A helpful way to study the way **regular verbs** change from one tense to another is to see them written in chart form. Fill out the chart, using the rules for forming tenses of regular verbs.

Present, plural, you or I	Present, singular	Present Participle, use with form of be	Past	Past Participle, use with form of have	Future, use with will
1. talk					
2. paint					
3. print					
4. crawl					
5. clean					
6. open					
7. cook					
8. pitch					
9. play					
10. work					
11. stop					
12. turn					
13. bat					
14. fix					
15. look					
16. watch					
17. wash					
18. smell					
19. smile					
20. enjoy					

Underline the verbs in the following sentences. In the space to the left, identify the tense as: Present, Present Participle, Past, Past Participle, or Future. (Some sentences have two verbs.)

_____ 1. The old man and his young friend were fixing a back door when they hear a large noise.
_____ 2. They glanced at each other immediately.
_____ 3. Mr. O'Brien turned toward the lake for a better view.
_____ 4. Jonathon had turned already to see who or what was making the noise.
_____ 5. They saw something moving under the tarpaulin that was covering the canoe.
_____ 6. Wondering what they will find, they walk slowly to the dock.
_____ 7. The tarp moved as several pieces of trash were pitched overboard.
_____ 8. Curiosity was getting the better of both of them.

EXTRA! Write two more sentences to finish the story above. Label the verbs you have chosen as Present, Present Participle, Past, Past Participle, or Future.

MP5093 - Grammar   **38**   Verbs

Write the past and past participle forms of each of the **regular verbs** listed below.

Present	Past	Past Participle (has, have, or had)
Example: help	helped	helped
1. file	_____	_____
2. hurry	_____	_____
3. sail	_____	_____
4. march	_____	_____
5. destroy	_____	_____
6. poke	_____	_____
7. rush	_____	_____

Follow the same procedure with the list of **irregular verbs**.

Example: do	did	done
1. ride	_____	_____
2. lose	_____	_____
3. swing	_____	_____
4. come	_____	_____
5. show	_____	_____
6. win	_____	_____
7. eat	_____	_____

In the blanks, write the past or past participle form of the verbs in parentheses.

1. (go) Alexander the Great _____ on many expeditions.
2. (drink) He _____ from the cup of poison hemlock.
3. (do) _____ the Greeks finally win the war?
4. (close) Angrily Hector _____ the flag of his tent.
5. (fly) Pegasus has _____ up to the palace.
6. (hide) The Trojan Horse _____ a surprise inside.
7. (know) The sailors had _____ the waves could be high.

Write five sentences. Use the noun and the appropriate form of the verb given below.

Helen, start

1. _____

soldiers, fight

2. _____

city, stand

3. _____

Greeks, collect

4. _____

women, see

5. _____

Harry's hint:

The verb **be** has many **different forms** in **different tenses**.

Examples:

Present	Past	Future
I **am**	I **was**	I **will be**
he, she, or it **is**	he, she, or it **was**	he, she, or it **will be**
we, you, or they **are**	we, you, or they **were**	we, you, or they **will be**
The painting **is** new.	The statue **was** Greek.	We **will be** studying art.

Am is only used with I.
Is is used with singular subjects, except you or I.
Are is used with plural subjects and you.

Was is used with singular subjects.
Were is used with singular subjects and you.

Use **will** with both singular and plural subjects.

In the following sentences, underline the forms of **be**.

1. The weather is cool.
2. We are happy to be going on a field trip.
3. I am anxious to see the display at the art museum.
4. The bus driver was late arriving at our school.
5. It was windy on the way downtown.
6. The exhibit will be on display all month.
7. Our teacher was ready to take attendance on the bus.
8. We will be happy to sketch some of the paintings.
9. The class was enthusiastic to learn about the special display.
10. The art museum directors were helpful as we walked through the large room.

In the following sentences, fill in the blanks with the correct **present** and **future tenses** of the verb **be**.

1. We _____ on our way to The Science House.
2. It _____ to be a terrific field trip.
3. The teacher _____ about to give final directions.
4. The first exhibit _____ one of the best.
5. We _____ surprised to see a student with his hair standing on end.
6. It _____ a demonstration of static electricity coming from a giant metal ball.
7. Several popular exhibits _____ _____ on the top floor.
8. One of my favorites _____ about response time in driving cars.
9. We _____ excited but tired after our morning at The Science House.
10. Our final adventure _____ _____ to zip down the two-story slide.

The verb **be** can serve as a helping verb before the **present participle**.
Example: We **are going** to a planetarium on our next field trip.

Write five sentences using am, is, are, was, and were as helping verbs with the present participles of these verbs: identify, travel, investigate, advise, and plan.

1. _____
2. _____
3. _____
4. _____
5. _____

Fill in the blanks with the proper form of the verbs **lie** or **lay**. Lie means to rest or recline. Lay means to put or place an object.

1. Please _____ the rope in the cargo bin.
2. The mate has _____ the ship's log on the captain's desk.
3. " _____ down!" shouted the captain.
4. The sailors _____ on deck all morning.
5. The strange ship has _____ idle in port for days.

The verb **sit** means to take a seat. **Set** means to put in position. If the proper form of **sit** or **set** is used in the sentence, write "correct" in the blank. If the verb form is not correct, cross out the verb and write the correct form in the blank.

_____ 1. The mermaids usually sit on rocks.
_____ 2. The men had sit the sails on the Argo.
_____ 3. Medea sat the magic potion under a tree.
_____ 4. Jason set down to think.
_____ 5. The mate had set the map in a safe place.

Underline the correct form of the verbs **let** and **leave** in parentheses below. **Let** means allow and **leave** means to go away from.

1. "You must (let, leave) my island now," shouted the giant.
2. Why did he (leave, left) the safety of the ship?
3. "(Leave, Let) me travel with you," said the young boy.
4. When Ulysses (leave, left), his wife cared for the farm.
5. When had he (left, let) the boy steer?

Fill in the blanks in the paragraphs below with the proper form of the verbs **teach** and **learn**. **Teach** means to show how. **Learn** means to gain knowledge.

The sailor brought a parrot on board ship. The rest of the men laughed and said, "You will never _____ that parrot anything."

"I will," said the sailor. "Parrots _____ to talk very quickly. You will see."

_____ did seem easy for the parrot. Every new word the sailor _____ the parrot was in its vocabulary by the next day. By the end of the week, the parrot _____ many new things. And so had the sailors.

Read the following paragraph. Circle any incorrect forms of lie, lay, sit, set, let, leave, teach, or learn.

At the end of the war, Ulysses left for his home in Ithaca. The journey was long and many dangers laid in his path. Even though the gods gave special protection to Ulysses and his men, evil creatures sit many traps. A ferocious, one-eyed giant known as Cyclops lie waiting. The boat passed the cave where Cyclops sat. The giant captured Ulysses and his men. He let them in the cave to die. But Ulysses had learn many tricks over the years, and he outsmarted the creature. He blinded Cyclops' one great eye, gathered his men, and safely left the cave.

How many errors did you find? _____

Name _____ Date _____

Prepositions are used to relate nouns or pronouns to other words in a sentence.

WORD BOX								
above	about	across	around	at	before	behind	below
beside	between	by	down	during	except	for	from
in	inside	into	like	near	of	on	over
through	to	under	until	up	with		

In the sentences below, fill in each blank with a suitable preposition from the Word Box.
1. Marta was waiting _____ her guide.
2. Together they would hike _____ the forest.
3. She had a large sandwich _____ her backpack.
4. Marta looked _____ the sky.
5. The sun was just rising _____ the edge of the mountain.
6. She hoped the guide would soon get _____ camp.
7. Suddenly, she saw the guide _____ the bushes.
8. She had not heard any sound _____ the guide.
9. Looking for animals should be easy _____ this skillful partner.
10. Marta was happy she had decided to come _____ this hike.

In each of the sentences, underline the words between which the preposition shows a relation.
Example: Marta went hiking in the woods.
1. They divided their lunch into two packages.
2. Marta followed the rules of the guide.
3. She hung her camera over her shoulder.
4. When a strange bird flew overhead, she took a picture of it.
5. Marta heard the sound of running water.
6. She and the guide sat on the riverbank.
7. The sandwiches were filled with ham and cheese.
8. The afternoon was the best part of the day.
9. In a tree branch, Marta found a rare bird's nest.
10. She would capture this moment on film.

A preposition and its object or objects and modifiers form a **prepositional phrase**.
Example: There are strange animals **in the dark jungle**. ("Jungle" is the object of the preposition.)

Write sentences using each of the following prepositional phrases.
1. with his sisters _____
2. near the ocean _____
3. up the dusty stairs _____
4. by a famous author _____
5. to the football field _____
6. in the gym _____
7. over her shoulders _____
8. on the windowsill _____
9. through the swamp _____
10. between the rows _____

On a separate sheet of paper, write at least five sentences that give directions for a walk through an imaginary forest. Describe the route from a riverbank to the top of a hill. Circle each preposition and underline each prepositional phrase.

Name _____   Date _____

Use the correct form of **prepositions**.

At means "presence in" and **to** means "motion toward."

Underline the correct preposition in each of the following sentences.
1. The girl walked (to, at) the pond.
2. Maria was (at, to) the gazebo.
3. Henry is not (at, to) home.
4. He has gone (at, to) a movie.
5. Vince drove the tractor (at, to) the barn.

6. Alvin was waiting (at, to) the door.
7. Were you (at, to) the beach?
8. I moved (at, to) Florida.
9. Shirley was not (at, to) the swim meet.
10. Let's not go (at, to) their house tonight.

Between is used for two persons or objects.
Among is used for more than two persons or objects.

In the sentences below, cross out the incorrect preposition.
1. Africa lies (between, among) two oceans.
2. (Between, Among) the three lions, there was not a single cub.
3. She distributed film (between, among) the camera crew.
4. Who will sit (between, among) the guide and the driver?
5. Food was divided (between, among) the five hunters.
6. There was one knapsack (between, among) the two women.
7. A meeting (between, among) the two was set for noon.
8. He disappeared (between, among) the crowd on the dock.
9. The ship anchored (between, among) two large yachts.
10. There were smaller cruisers (between, among) the boats.

Beside means "next to." **Besides** means "in addition to."

In the sentences below, circle the correct preposition.
1. Have you any money (beside, besides) your allowance?
2. The forest stretches (beside, besides) the river for many miles.
3. (Beside, Besides) the two jeeps, they have a small car.
4. The big dog lay (beside, besides) the campfire.
5. (Beside, Besides) being a good runner, Leona was a superior student.

From means "out of." **Off** is the opposite of "on."

In the sentences below, underline the correct preposition.
1. George got his lunch (from, off) his locker.
2. Keep (from, off) the grass.
3. Henry jumped (from, off) the stone wall.

4. Get an ax (from, off) the trunk.
5. Get (from, off) there right now!

In means "contained by." **Into** means "forward and within."

In the sentences below, cross out the incorrect preposition.
1. The two of them ran (in, into) the forest.
2. The clock (in, into) the dining room is always wrong.
3. Anna dropped the stone (in, into) the stream.
4. The vines (in, into) the forest are thick as ropes.
5. All the students (in, into) my class participated in the discussion.

On a separate sheet of paper, write three sentences for each of the following prepositions: at, between, besides, off, and into.

Harry's hints:
   A **preposition** is a word that is used to relate a noun or a pronoun to other words in a sentence. A **prepositional phrase** answers several questions: **how, when, where, which one,** or **how many**.
   Some words may be used as adverbs in some sentences; however, other times they may be the first word of a **prepositional phrase**.
Examples: There are many clouds **above**. (**Above** is an **adverb** that tells **where** the clouds are.)
   There were many clouds **above our heads**. (**Above** is used as the first word of a prepositional phrase that tells **where** the clouds are.)

Choose a preposition from the Word Box to complete each sentence below. The words in parentheses will tell which kind of word to choose.

WORD BOX

above	about	across	around	at	before
behind	below	beside	between	by	down
during	except	for	from	in	inside
into	like	near	of	on	over
through	to	under	until	up	with

1. We arrived _____ the field a little early. (where)
2. The crowd was gathering _____ the colorful balloons. (where)
3. We had won a special prize _____ a contest. (how)
4. The prize was a ride _____ a hot air balloon. (where)
5. The contest was sponsored _____ a large bank. (how)
6. _____ the ride could begin, the wind had to die down. (when)
7. We climbed _____ the gondola carefully. (where)
8. It was smaller _____ the basket than I thought. (where)
9. The pilot stood _____ me as he shouted commands to his ground crew. (where)
10. The flight began as we began to rise _____ the crowd. (where)

The **object of the preposition** is a **noun** or **pronoun**.
Example: The balloon was **above** the **ground**. (**Ground** is the object of the preposition **above**.)

In the sentences below, underline the prepositional phrase and circle the object of the preposition. (There may be more than one prepositional phrase in each sentence.)
1. The flight was beginning around the park.
2. We started drifting across the river.
3. The balloon with colorful stripes was near our balloon.
4. I was still surprised by the small space inside the gondola.
5. There was so much to see from our vantage point.
6. After an hour we were nearing our landing area.

Write a paragraph describing the position of an object in the room. Underline all of the prepositional phrases in the paragraph.

Name _____ Date _____

A **prepositional phrase** can modify a noun or a pronoun just as an **adjective** does. It answers the questions **which one**, **how many**, or **what kind**.
Example: The film **about an African safari** was fascinating. (The prepositional phrase tells what kind of film it was.)

In each sentence, underline the prepositional phrase and circle the noun or pronoun it modifies.
1. The tallest mountain in Africa is Kilimanjaro.
2. Herds of wild animals live in the grasslands.
3. Shipments of gold are frequent.
4. The large amount of rain produces dense forests.
5. Many of the colorful birds live there.
6. Rivers with many rapids run swiftly.
7. Safaris into the jungle are popular.
8. Ancient people left rock paintings of animals.
9. Packs of vicious dogs sometimes attack zebras.
10. Visitors from many countries come here.

Expand the following sentences by adding a prepositional phrase used as an adjective.
Example: The girl walked quickly. The girl **in the blue dress** walked quickly.
1. The house was very old. _____
2. The fire went out. _____
3. Many wanted a holiday. _____
4. The road was rocky. _____
5. The box was very heavy. _____
6. The leaves fluttered. _____

A **prepositional phrase** may also act as an **adverb**. It answers the questions **how**, **when**, or **where**.

In the sentences below, underline the prepositional phrases that act as adverbs. Write the verbs that they modify in the blanks.
Example: ___met___ The group met at the park's entrance.
_____ 1. Rangers drove them into the compounds.
_____ 2. They walked to the nearest campsite.
_____ 3. The safari members found firewood in the forest.
_____ 4. All helped at dinnertime.
_____ 5. The meat turned slowly on the spit.
_____ 6. They raised their tents around the campfire.
_____ 7. Firelight shone on the nearby trees.
_____ 8. Jungle animals stayed out of sight.
_____ 9. They all slept in their sleeping bags.
_____ 10. The stars shone above them.

Some adverbs double as prepositions. In the sentences below, determine if the word in boldface is an adverb or a preposition. Write an **A** for adverb or a **P** for preposition in the blanks.
__ 1. They left the compound soon **after**.
__ 2. The guides went home **after** lunch.
__ 3. They drove **down** the forest trail.
__ 4. Quickly the sun went **down**.
__ 5. He fixed the tire **before** the trip.
__ 6. They had never seen such plants **before**.
__ 7. One guide walked **behind**.
__ 8. He saw a lion **behind** a bush.
__ 9. They waited **outside** for several minutes.
__ 10. They were **outside** the game preserve boundaries.

Harry's hints:
> **Adjectives** can be used to compare nouns.
> Rule 1: Add **er** to most adjectives to compare two nouns.
>   Example: short   shorter
>   Add **est** to most adjectives to compare more than two nouns.
>   Example: tall   tallest
> Rule 2: When a word ends in silent **e**, drop the **e** before adding **er** or **est**.
>   Example: blue   bluer   bluest
> Rule 3: When a word ends with one consonant with one vowel before it, double the final consonant before adding **er** or **est**.
>   Example: mad   madder   maddest
> Rule 4: When a word ends with **y**, change the **y** to **i** before adding **er** or **est**.
>   Example: funny   funnier   funniest
> Rule 5: With long adjectives, use **more** or **most** before the adjective.
>   Example: beautiful   more beautiful   most beautiful

Write the two forms of comparisons for each word. In the parentheses, write the number of the rule used.

	Between two nouns	More than two nouns	Rule
1. quick	_____	_____	( )
2. long	_____	_____	( )
3. mean	_____	_____	( )
4. rare	_____	_____	( )
5. high	_____	_____	( )
6. wide	_____	_____	( )
7. silly	_____	_____	( )
8. big	_____	_____	( )
9. flat	_____	_____	( )
10. expensive	_____	_____	( )

Add **er** or **est** to the adjectives in parentheses, and write them in the blanks.

1. This mixing bowl is the _____ I own. (big)

2. We are going to make a _____ batch of pancakes than we did yesterday. (large)

3. Please pass me the _____ of the two spoons in the drawer. (long)

4. You look _____ than I do with that flour on your nose. (silly)

5. The oven needs to be _____ to make cookies than pies. (hot)

6. We need the cookie sheet that is on the _____ shelf in the cabinet. (low)

7. I think I am _____ than you are. (hungry)

8. I will need the _____ hot pad to pick up the hot cookie sheet. (heavy)

EXTRA!

Write a paragraph comparing the subjects you study in school. Use a variety of adjectives ending in **er** and **est**.

Harry's hint:
Adjectives describe nouns by telling **how many** or **what kind**.

Underline the adjectives in each sentence.
Example: The writer told <u>many, interesting</u> stories about Mark Twain.

1. Mark Twain was the pen name of one of America's best and well-known authors.

2. His real name was Samuel Clemens.

3. He wrote humorous stories about ordinary people.

4. Samuel Clemens worked as a newspaper cub reporter and as an adventurous riverboat pilot.

5. Later, he chose the name Mark Twain as his pen name, using a riverboating phrase that means "safe water—twelve feet deep."

6. He married, had four children, and built a spectacular home in Connecticut.

7. He earned a good part of his income from lecturing.

8. <u>The Adventures of Tom Sawyer</u> was his first novel, and it contains the famous scene about the white-washed fence.

9. <u>The Adventures of Huckleberry Finn</u> is a story about a runaway boy, Huck Finn, and a slave named Jim.

10. Mark Twain's enormous popularity as a fascinating writer increased after his death.

Some adjectives are overused. People often describe things with the words "good" or "bad."
Choose better words from the Word Bank to write five sentences.
Example: There was a bad storm. There was a terrible storm.

WORD BANK	good: excellent, wonderful, perfect, marvelous bad: horrible, terrible, hideous, dreadful

1. _____

2. _____

3. _____

4. _____

5. _____

EXTRA!

Make up a mystery story using the group of objects listed below. Use adjectives to help your listener form a better mental picture of the setting and the action in your story.
Objects: an unsigned postcard, a hollowed-out book, a locket on a gold chain, and a broken pocket watch

Name _____   Date _____

> Harry's hint:
> **Adjectives** are used to describe how we see, hear, feel, smell, and taste things.

An acrostic poem uses a noun written vertically on the left side of your paper. Then each letter is used to begin a word or a phrase describing the noun. Follow the example of the poem "SNOW" and write an acrostic poem about summer. A dictionary or thesaurus is helpful for this type of writing project.

S   ilent as it falls
N   oiseless in the night
O   n the landscape
W   hite and beautiful

S _____
U _____
M _____
M _____
E _____
R _____

Write an acrostic poem on a separate paper, using the letters in your name written vertically down the side of the paper. Use words to describe yourself.

H   umorous hound
A   greeable to all
R   eady with helpful hints
R   eally a good friend to
Y   ou and me!

A personal gift to a good friend would be a birthday card with an acrostic poem with his/her name and descriptive phrases about him/her. Decorate the card and you will have a unique gift.

Nouns and adjectives usually go together to make clear mental pictures. Sometimes they can be very humorous, especially when they rhyme. Write the number of the following descriptions in front of the matching "rare pairs."

Descriptions
1. foolish flower
2. trained tiger
3. fat dog
4. nice pig
5. extra shoes
6. chubby insect
7. white bird
8. courageous soldier
9. greasy chicken
10. discovered noise

Rare Pairs
___ tame game
___ brave knave
___ fat gnat
___ pale quail
___ crazy daisy
___ slick chick
___ found sound
___ spare pair
___ round hound
___ fine swine

> Write your own descriptive phrase and illustrate it on the front of a blank 3" x 5" index card. Write the "rare pair" on the back of the card. Make a class booklet of all the cards to have a good laugh!

Harry's hint:
   Adjectives that are made from **proper nouns** are called **proper adjectives**. They begin with **capital letters**.
Example: Do you like Italian food?

Underline the proper adjective and write it correctly.

1. I ate a danish pastry for breakfast. _____
2. We sailed on a german ship. _____
3. The students wrote a french play. _____
4. The belgian tourist asked us about World War II. _____
5. Michigan is on the canadian border. _____
6. We ate at a chinese restaurant. _____
7. Our tour guide took us to the british countryside. _____
8. We even ate swedish meatballs. _____
9. The children in the spanish school were very friendly. _____
10. The south american native explained how to make fajitas. _____

   Rewrite each sentence below to use a proper adjective.
Example: My father bought a car from Japan.
         My father bought a Japanese car.

1. The art from Alaska was on display in the museum.

_____

2. The tea from Britain was served with cream and sugar.

_____

3. The freighter from Liberia steamed into port.

_____

4. The flu from Asia is making many persons ill.

_____

5. The food from America is more plain than French cuisine.

_____

   Write five sentences using proper adjectives. Choose words from the Word Bank. Write about a trip you have taken or one you wish you could take someday.

WORD BANK	European	Missourian	Greek	French
	Israeli	Texan	North American	Irish

1. _____
2. _____
3. _____
4. _____
5. _____

Adjectives modify nouns or pronouns.

Underline all the adjectives found in the paragraph below. Answer the questions following the paragraph.

The Japanese people celebrate many ancient festivals. On May 5th, there is a special way to honor the boys in a family. A tall flagpole is placed in the yard of a home. On it are colorful flags that look like toy fish. Each flying fish stands for one boy in the family. If there are six sons in the family, there are six flags on the pole. This old custom means that the Japanese hope for brave, strong boys in the family.

1. Which adjective describes the flagpole? _____

2. Which two adjectives describe the kind of boys the Japanese want for their families? _____

3. Name two adjectives that describe fish. _____

Next to each noun below, write the adjective(s) that modifies it.

festivals _____ way _____ custom _____

Draw one line under each adjective in the paragraph below. Then answer the questions that follow.

Japanese girls have a special day as well. On March 3rd, a girl invites her favorite friends to her home. She puts beautiful dresses on all her dolls. She sets up tiny doll furniture on a platform. Her friends enjoy the pretty display. Afterwards, they also enjoy delicious cakes and fruit.

1. Which two adjectives describe the furniture? _____

2. What adjective tells about the refreshments? _____

Next to each adjective below, write the noun it modifies.

favorite _____ pretty _____ beautiful _____

For each of the following nouns, choose three descriptive adjectives. Each one should give the noun a different meaning.

Example: house—haunted, elegant, tiny

1. river _____
2. child _____
3. cookie _____
4. city _____
5. garden _____
6. song _____
7. beach _____
8. conversation _____

EXTRA! Select a short paragraph from a book or story you have recently read. On another sheet of paper, make a list of all of the adjectives in the paragraph. Next to the adjective, write the noun it describes.

An **adjective** modifies a noun or pronoun. In each phrase, underline the adjective. Rewrite the phrase two times using new adjectives. On the first line, make the new adjective a synonym; on the second line, make it an antonym.

	Synonym	Antonym
Example: loud noise	roaring noise	soft noise
1. bad trip	_____	_____
2. poor woman	_____	_____
3. nice time	_____	_____
4. small dog	_____	_____
5. red blood	_____	_____
6. mean man	_____	_____
7. dirty children	_____	_____
8. good lemonade	_____	_____
9. funny clown	_____	_____
10. empty park	_____	_____

Underline the adjectives in the following letter. Rewrite the letter on another piece of paper, substituting adjectives whenever possible.

January 15, 1944

My friend,

I suppose you have heard about our incredible escape. I thought you might like to hear more details. I was taken prisoner and sent to Stalag Luft III, a German camp. While in the camp, I began to ponder various methods of escape.

Since we were allowed to have daily exercise, this seemed to be an ideal time. Every day we pushed a wooden vaulting horse into the prison yard. We had built the horse out of old Red Cross packing crates. Long wooden beams ran through the center of the crates so that four strong men could carry the horse to its place in the dusty exercise yard of the prison.

What the solemn guards did not know was that hidden inside the vaulting horse was a man. When the horse was placed on the ground, the man inside opened a trap door and began the arduous job of tunneling through the clay into the sandy soil below the vault. At the appointed time, the prisoner, carrying bags of yellow sand, climbed back into the horse. Eventually we sent two men down to speed the tedious work. A pulley system was developed. The constant vaulting shored up the sand above the tunnel and also masked the noise of the tunnelers. The Germans used seismographs to uncover any tunneling efforts, but vaulting masked the slight tremors made by tunnelers.

On October 29, Michael Codner, Oliver Philpot, and I were ready to make an escape attempt. Michael was sealed underground for two hours. During this time he was forced to make a microscopic air hole in the sand. We wore long, hooded clothes that we had dyed black with dark coffee grounds. At 6 P.M., the remaining prisoners led a noisy diversion as we made our way through the tunnel to the land beyond the wall. I expected to be caught. I was ready for the sudden crack of a bullet, but when we reached the surface there was no sound. We were free! We made our way home to loved ones and friends.

Your friend,
Eric Williams

This, **that**, **these**, and **those** are demonstrative adjectives that modify nouns. They should not be used with **here** and **there**.

Cross out any incorrect or unnecessary words in the following sentences

1. These here flowers are fresh from the garden.
2. Watch your step on those there stones.
3. Where did you find that there shovel?
4. Put the plants in this here box.

Draw a line under each noun that the word in boldfaced type modifies.

1. **This** automobile factory has two owners.
2. Dad can buy a sports car from **that** salesperson.
3. **These** keys will open the trunk.
4. **Those** tires are brand new.

Write two sentences for each word: this, that, these, those.

1. _____
2. _____
3. _____
4. _____
5. _____
6. _____
7. _____
8. _____

Some words are used as **adjectives** and **nouns**.

In front of each sentence, write an **A** if the word in boldfaced type is used as an adjective and an **N** if it is used as a noun.

Examples: _A_ Fish are put in **ice** chests right away.
_N_ The fishermen pile chipped **ice** on top of the salmon.
1. ___ The **winter** wind sweeps down the mountain.
2. ___ **Winter** brings snow to Japan's northernmost island.
3. ___ The Tokyo Temple is a modern **building**.
4. ___ Farmers use straw and wood as **building** materials.

Write sentences using the following words as both adjectives and nouns: fish, boat, oil, rich.

1. _____
2. _____
3. _____
4. _____
5. _____
6. _____
7. _____
8. _____

Name _____ Date _____

Write the **comparative** and **superlative** degrees of the following **adjectives**. Use more or most before longer adjectives. Follow the example.

Positive Degree	Comparative Degree	Superlative Degree
Example: small	smaller	smallest
1. big		
2. green		
3. long		
4. fast		
5. young		
6. happy		
7. late		
8. wonderful		
9. difficult		
10. honest		

In each of the following sentences, underline the adjectives that show comparison. Write a **C** for adjectives in the comparative degree and an **S** for those in the superlative degree in the blanks.

1. ___ Tokyo is the largest city in Japan.
2. ___ A "Bullet Train" offers faster transportation than a car.
3. ___ Mt. Fuji is the country's highest mountain.
4. ___ The island of Hokkaido is one of the most important fishing centers in the world.
5. ___ Buddhism is a more popular religion in Japan than Confucianism.

Complete the table below with the appropriate degree of each adjective.

Positive Degree	Comparative Degree	Superlative Degree
1. ___	___	worst
2. ___	nicer	___
3. messy	___	___
4. ___	___	largest
5. ___	better	___

Write three sentences. Use adjectives to compare two cars, two cities, and two boats. Use the proper form of adjectives chosen from the following words: fast, large, busy, dangerous, old.

1. _____
2. _____
3. _____

EXTRA! Use books and other resources to learn more about Japan and its neighboring countries. Write a few sentences comparing Japan to other countries in Asia. Use the superlative degree of at least one adjective in each sentence.

MP5093 - Grammar   **53**   Adjectives

Name _____ Date _____

Using the atmosphere of your classroom, list items that appeal to the following senses. Put one of each in a sentence.

1. Appearance   Example: blue walls

_____ _____ _____ _____

_____

2. Sound   Example: school bell

_____ _____ _____ _____

3. Smell   Example: chalk dust

_____ _____ _____ _____

4. Texture   Example: smooth desktop

_____ _____ _____ _____

_____

Using varying degrees of a modifier makes your writing more vivid. Following the example below, fill in blanks of a rising scale of description. A thesaurus is a helpful tool for this exercise.
Example: bad   mean   wicked   vicious   murderous

1. strong _____ _____ _____ overpowering
2. good _____ _____ _____ _____
3. sick _____ _____ _____ _____

Write a paragraph describing the scene in the gymnasium during a physical education class. Recall how it looks, smells, feels, and sounds. Make good use of descriptive and exciting words.

_____

_____

_____

_____

_____

_____

_____

Pretend you are in the kitchen preparing a pizza. Think about the sights, sounds, smells, tastes, and textures of the ingredients as you create the ultimate pizza. Be as descriptive as possible in the paragraph.

_____

_____

_____

_____

_____

_____

_____

_____

A **phrase** is a **group of related words** used as a **single part of speech**. A phrase can be used as an **adjective** to describe a noun. Example: **Silver** bracelets jangled on her wrist. ("Silver" is an adjective.)
Bracelets **of silver** jangled on her wrist. ("Of silver" is a phrase used as an adjective.)

Underline each phrase used as an adjective. Circle the noun it modifies.
1. Louis XIV was a French king of extraordinary power.
2. The palace at Versailles is a building of lasting beauty.
3. The years of the French Revolution were hard on the poor.
4. Napoleon Bonaparte was a general of the French Army.
5. Members of his troops followed him across the mountains.
6. For years, Lyon has been famous for the manufacture of silk.
7. Silk is often used in dresses of high style.
8. Paris is usually known as the leader of fashion.
9. French designers annually cause a stir among dress buyers.
10. The business of fashion design is a highly competitive one.

Change the adjectives in boldfaced type to phrases describing the nouns.
1. **Courageous** soldiers crossed the Alps. _____
2. The **mountain** path was very steep. _____
3. **Concrete** roads would have been helpful. _____
4. Generals must be **strong** leaders. _____
5. The **green** house was a rendezvous point. _____

Change the following adjectives to descriptive phrases and add appropriate nouns.
Example: gentle—a touch of such gentleness
1. brave _____
2. interesting _____
3. spring _____
4. worried _____
5. weak _____
6. musical _____
7. tin _____
8. wooden _____
9. fearful _____
10. joyful _____
11. charming _____
12. boastful _____

Add appropriate adjective phrases in the following blanks.
1. A soldier _____ would never disobey.
2. The first leader _____ was popular.
3. Uniforms _____ were expensive.
4. Baskets _____ were thrown to the poor.
5. The trip _____ was over 100 miles.
6. The streets _____ were lit with burning branches.

EXTRA! Choose an advertisement from a magazine or newspaper. Change any adjectives found in the ad to descriptive phrases. Redraw your ad with these new phrases.

"I love to run," Harry said swiftly.

Harry's hints:
   Adverbs give meaning to sentences by telling **how, where**, or **when** the action is taking place. Some sentences are called "Swifties" because of their frequent use in an old-time book series, called <u>The Adventures of Tom Swift</u>. Their humor came from the clever use of adverbs.

Examples: "Pass me the **knife**," she said **sharply.**
         "I forgot to **starch** your shirt," she said **stiffly.**

   To write "Swifties," write a sentence of dialogue, and then think of an adverb that relates to the action of the verb.

   Write the adverb that makes the following sentences humorous.

ADVERBS:				
wisely	stuffily	blankly	colorfully	crossly
sharply	rapidly	dryly	lightly	sweetly

1. "Please pass me the honey," she said _____ .
2. "Hand me a crayon," he said _____ .
3. "I don't want to play tic-tac-toe," she answered _____ ,
4. "Pass the lemonade," Tom said _____ .
5. "I've been dieting," Sue said _____ .
6. "I have a terrible head cold," George complained _____ .
7. "I'm going to run in the Boston Marathon," Bruce said _____ .
8. "I'm having trouble filling out this application," Jesse said _____ .
9. "I hear the owl hooting," Ginger exclaimed _____ .
10. "My spear is very sharp," said the warrior _____ .

   Write your own "Swifties," using the following adverbs:

   hoarsely   flatly   sourly   hotly   wildly   roughly

1. _____
2. _____
3. _____
4. _____
5. _____
6. _____

Name _____ Date _____

Harry's hint:
    An **adverb** tells about a verb. It tells **how, when**, or **where** something is done.
Examples:
    HOW: We walked **quickly** to the auditorium.
    WHEN: The magician performed **early** in the day.
    WHERE: His assistant walked **home**.

how
when
where

Circle the adverbs in the sentences. Write **how, when**, or **where** in the blank at the end of the sentence to tell about the adverb.

1. The magic show was beginning in the auditorium soon.   _____

2. We were so excited to see the curtain raise quickly.   _____

3. The magician appeared below the puff of smoke.   _____

4. He made many objects disappear smoothly.   _____

5. We watched his sleight of hand closely.   _____

6. Sometimes he made us laugh at his tricks.   _____

7. His skilled hand movements, called prestidigitation, were practiced well.   _____

8. Then he made a lighted electric bulb appear overhead.   _____

9. Afterwards, the performer gave a talk about Harry Houdini.   _____

10. The magic show ended after he made himself disappear.   _____

Complete the following sentences by using an adverb that answers the question **how, when,** or **where** something is done.

1. The magician performed his tricks _____ WHERE?

2. An audience member was brought on stage _____ WHEN?

3. The magician disappeared _____ HOW?

4. He made a rabbit appear _____ WHERE?

5. _____ he ended the show. HOW?

Write five sentences using one adverb from the Adverb Bank in each sentence. Tell what question it answers: HOW, WHEN, WHERE?

ADVERB BANK	then	easily	suddenly	up	down
	badly	excitedly	better	finally	high
	inside	before	quickly	seriously	there
	now	happily	usually	out	later

1. _____

2. _____

3. _____

4. _____

5. _____

Adverbs of place tell **where**. They usually modify verbs.

Complete each sentence by adding an adverb of place from the list.
Example: Clouds hung **low** over Mt. Fuji.

upward   under   back and forth   everywhere   inside

1. Boats sail _____ from the mainland to Japan.
2. Shoes are removed before the family walks _____ .
3. Pearl divers find thousands of oysters _____ the water.
4. Gongs and drums are heard _____ their music group plays.
5. Movie production is moving _____ on the list of Japanese arts.

Read the paragraph below. Underline the adverbs of place.

The group of mountain climbers gathered at the beginning of the trail. Soon they would be going up the steep path to the top of the mountain. The top looked far away and it probably was. The group began to gather their equipment. The backpacks and climbing gear lay nearby. But cooking utensils were scattered here and there. At last everything was packed. The climbers sat down on handy rocks and waited for their guide.

Adverbs of manner tell **how**.

Write the number of an adverb of manner in the left column in front of an appropriate verb in the right column.

1. fearlessly   ___ slept
2. happily   ___ recommended
3. knowingly   ___ danced
4. thoroughly   ___ read the books
5. soundly   ___ climbed the mountain
6. prettily   ___ took a chance
7. strongly   ___ received the prize
8. heartily   ___ laughed

Choose one of the above combinations of verb and adverb. Create a person who would have acted in such a way. Determine why he or she won a prize or climbed a mountain, etc. Tell about it in five or more sentences. Give your paragraph a title. Share the story with a friend.

_____
_____
_____
_____
_____
_____
_____
_____
_____

Name _____   Date _____

Adverbs modify verbs, adjectives, or other adverbs. Adverbs are used to answer the questions: how, when, where, why, how often, and how much.

In these short phrases, underline the adverb and circle the word it modifies. On the first line, tell whether the adverb modifies a verb, adjective, or adverb. On the second line, tell what question the adverb answers. There are two phrases with two adverbs.

		Word Modified	Question Answered
1. <u>frequently</u> (left) home		**verb**	**when**
2. spoke too quickly		_____	_____
3. spoke too quickly		_____	_____
4. nowadays we understand		_____	_____
5. was finally happy		_____	_____
6. plane swooped down		_____	_____
7. team won easily		_____	_____
8. dances quite gracefully		_____	_____
9. dances quite gracefully		_____	_____
10. totally inappropriate behavior		_____	_____

Underline the adverbs in the following sentences. Circle the word the adverb modifies, and draw an arrow from the adverb to the word .

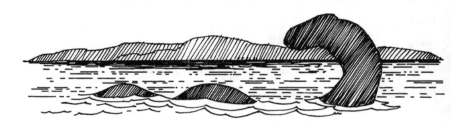

1. Loch Ness, in Scotland, is eerily quiet.
2. The lake never freezes, although it is certainly cold enough.
3. The loch, full of slimy, dark peat moss, is usually black and thick.
4. Alert villagers occasionally report the sighting of a ghost ship.
5. The ship, seen only late at night, is not lighted and mysteriously vanishes.
6. One of the first Loch Ness monster stories apparently surfaced in 565 A.D.
7. Until about 1930, villagers seldom talked about the great beast living in their midst.
8. It was during the 1930s that publicity about the monster spread quickly around the world.
9. Over 12,000 stories have been told, but only a small percentage of these were actually studied or documented.
10. In 1934, Dr. R. Kenneth Wilson was vacationing at Loch Ness when he suddenly saw swirling waters in the lake.
11. He immediately grabbed his camera and snapped several pictures of the famed Loch Ness monster.
12. The resulting photos were then published around the world and remain the clearest and most graphic pictures available anywhere.

Pretend you have just sighted the famous Loch Ness monster. Write a brief description of your experience. Underline all adverbs and circle the words that they modify.

Name _____   Date _____

Adverbs are used to **compare time** or **kinds of actions**.
Example: Ramón arrived **early**.

In the blanks, write the correct form of the adverb listed in front of each sentence.

intensely   1. Flower arranging is studied _____ in Japan than in most other
                  countries.

well   2. Master arrangers must handle flowers and branches _____ of all in
                  the class.

carefully   3. The first branch is placed in the vase _____ of all.

efficiently   4. The older gardener works _____ than the younger one.

Write a sentence comparing the actions of two persons for each of the adverbs.
Example: far— Mary ran **farther** than Sarah.

late _____

well _____

badly _____

joyfully _____

Write a sentence comparing the actions of more than two persons for each of the adverbs.
Example: Louise ran the **farthest** in the class.

late _____

well _____

badly _____

joyfully _____

In the following limericks by Edward Lear, underline any adverb that can be used to compare
action. Write its three comparative forms in the blanks.

There was an old person of Cromer
Who stood on one leg to read Homer
    When he found he grew stiff
    He jumped over the cliff,
Which concluded that person of Cromer.

There was an old man, who when little
Fell casually into a kettle;
    But, growing too stout
    He could never get out,
So he passed all his life in that kettle.

Write your own limerick in the same style as Edward Lear. Underline any adverb that
can be used to compare actions and write its three comparative forms.

Adverbs modify verbs.

Match each of the verbs in the first line below with an appropriate adverb. Write the number of the verb in the blank in front of the best choice of adverb.

1. run   2. skate   3. jump   4. lie   5. eat
___ down   ___ away   ___ often   ___ up   ___ over

Add to the meaning of each of these sentences by choosing an adverb. It should answer the question in parentheses before each sentence.

1. (How) The driver _____ stopped the car.
2. (Where) Unfortunately, the car was facing _____ .
3. (When) The crew _____ moved the racer to the side of the track.
4. (How much) They perspired _____ as they changed the tire.

Adverbs of time tell **when** or **how often**. They usually modify verbs.

In the following sentences, draw one line under each adverb of time and two lines under the verb it modifies.

1. Yesterday Sam forgot his homework.
2. Susie never borrows anything.
3. Sally always brings her lunch.
4. Suddenly the fire alarm rang.

Using the following adverbs of time, write a five sentence paragraph about an action sport you have watched.

immediately   finally   soon   tomorrow   sometimes

_____
_____
_____
_____
_____
_____
_____
_____
_____

Adverbs of degree tell **how much** or **how little**.

Use each of the following adverbs of degree in a sentence. The sentences should all refer to one of the players of the sport described in the paragraph above.

merely   almost   quite   very   nearly

1. _____
2. _____
3. _____
4. _____
5. _____

Name _____   Date _____

   In the exercise below, write the adjectives and adverbs under the correct
headings to the left of the sentences.

Adjectives	Adverbs	
_____	_____	1. The young teacher collected our papers quickly.
_____	_____	2. We closely watched as she measured the thick stack of papers.
_____	_____	3. The quiet class noticed that she placed them momentarily on her desk.
_____	_____	4. She then placed them on a large scale.
_____	_____	5. As we carefully watched, she read the arrow on the metric scale.
_____	_____	6. She told the interested class that our papers weighed nearly one kilogram.
_____	_____	7. We learned later that our next math class would be about the metric system.
_____	_____	8. The United States is clearly becoming the last country to adopt the system.
_____	_____	9. Amazingly, we learned that the metric system is easier to remember than our customary system.
_____	_____	10. We spent our next class enthusiastically measuring everything in our classroom.

Adjectives answer three questions: what kind, how many, or which one?

   Complete the following sentences by using these adjectives that answer the questions in
parentheses: quiet, glass, plastic, five, seven, good, intelligent, wooden, large, small, tall, three.
1. The _____ boy sitting next to me asked a question about the metric system. (which one?)
2. The teacher answered, complimenting him on his _____ question. (which one?)
3. We spent the next half hour measuring _____ friends' height. (how many?)
4. We also learned that our _____ rulers were labeled with centimeters rather than inches. (what kind?)
5. It was fun pouring tinted water into _____ vials to see how much was one liter. (what kind?)

   Adverbs also answer three questions by: how, when, or where?
   Complete the following sentences using these adverbs that answer the questions in
parentheses: easily, later, tomorrow, quickly, anywhere, cheerfully, inside, upstairs, quietly.
1. I _____ measured Yung Moon's wrist and wrote down the measurement in centimeters. (how?)
2. Each pair of students could work _____. (where?)
3. The teacher asked us to turn in our measurement lists _____. (when?)
4. We discovered she was planning to have us remeasure ourselves _____ to see how much we had grown. (when?)
5. Our lessons on the metric system were designed to help us see how _____ it worked. (how?)

Name _____ Date _____

A **phrase** is a **group of related words** used as a **single part of speech**. A **phrase** can act as an **adverb** to tell about a verb.
Example: The horse plunged **down the hill**. ("Down the hill" tells where the horse plunged.)

Complete each of the following sentences by adding a prepositional phrase used as an adverb. In the blank, write if the phrase tells **where**, **when**, or **how** the action happens.

_____   1. The snow fell _____
_____   2. Spring flowers bloom _____
_____   3. The couple strolled _____
_____   4. The waiter served _____
_____   5. Put the books _____
_____   6. Yachts sail _____
_____   7. A tiny kitten crouched _____
_____   8. Two chairs were placed _____
_____   9. A magnificent painting hung _____
_____ 10. Derek trudged _____

Use each of the following prepositional phrases as an adverb in a sentence.
1. under the tree
_____

2. while she knitted
_____

3. by opening the door
_____

4. to the grocer
_____

5. in the tropics
_____

6. on every corner
_____

7. with a new key
_____

8. beside his master
_____

9. behind the lamp
_____

10. above his head
_____

In the following paragraphs, underline all of the phrases used as adverbs.

France is a colorful and interesting country in Europe. Each region of France has its own specialty. Ways of speaking, cooking, plowing, and dressing differ from region to region.

Brittany is on the Atlantic Coast where the wind blows with great force. Fishermen throw their lines in the water and hope for a good catch. The beautiful Riviera lies on the Mediterranean coast. Its cliff towns and beaches bask in warm sunlight.

In the chateaux country of the Loire Valley, castles stand on rock foundations. Normandy manufactures apple brandy and champagne. Frenchmen work with grapes to make their famous wines. Although each region is unique in some ways, Paris remains the real center of French life.

On a separate sheet of paper, write two descriptive sentences about a city with which you are familiar. Include at least one prepositional phrase used as an adverb.

Name _____ Date _____

Harry's hints:
   Personification is a **figure of speech** that gives human characteristics to inanimate objects, animals, or abstract ideas. The use of personification makes writing and storytelling more interesting.
Example: The dishes glared at me from the sink. (Dishes cannot glare, but when they take on this human characteristic, it helps create a clearer picture for the reader.)

   In each blank below, write the letter of the word that would create personification for the word or phrase.

a. danced   c. screamed   e. whistled   g. chewed
b. crawled   d. groaned   f. cried   h. sang
___ garbage disposal   ___ the chair   ___ fog   ___ wind chimes
___ the wind   ___ the candlelight   ___ the rain clouds ___ sirens

   Write sentences for five of the matching pairs.
Example: The garbage disposal chewed up the old bones.
1. _____
2. _____
3. _____
4. _____
5. _____

   A **hyperbole** is a figure of speech that uses exaggeration to express a point. It is not to be taken literally.
Example: It was so hot today that I could fry an egg on the sidewalk!

   Complete the sentences below to create hyperboles. Use these words: bucket, truck, steam, sky, teacher, mile, star, elephant, ears, rock.
 1. I am so hungry that I could eat an __ __ __ __ __ __ __ __!
 2. Make me a sandwich a __ __ __ __ high.
 3. I am so sad, I could cry a __ __ __ __ __ __ __ ful of tears.
 4. The pizza was so large, we had to bring it home in a __ __ __ __ __.
 5. His father was so angry, __ __ __ __ __ came out of his ears.
 6. The rock group was so loud, our __ __ __ __ fell off.
 7. The stale bread is hard as a __ __ __ __.
 8. The play was so bad, the __ __ __ __ went home.
 9. The class was so boring, the __ __ __ __ __ __ __ fell asleep.
10. I jumped so high, I touched the __ __ __.

   Use the following phrases to write your own hyperboles. Be sure to really exaggerate!
1. It snowed so hard _____
2. The wrestler was so powerful _____
3. The comedian was so funny _____
4. On my birthday I was so happy _____
5. I ate so much _____
6. The race car was so fast _____

EXTRA!
   Write your own hyperbole about something you do after school. Draw a picture to illustrate your hyperbole.

Words that have the **same or similar** meanings are called **synonyms**. Increase your writing skills by replacing uninteresting and vague words with exact, descriptive ones.
Example: The sound of the siren was **loud**. (vague)
   The sound of the siren was **shrill and piercing**. (exact)

In the following sentences, underline all descriptive words.
1. Crimson flames swept through the forest.
2. Grim, exhausted firefighters struggled to control the fire.
3. Limbs crashed heavily to the ground.
4. Startled animals fled.
5. Rain began to splash on the hissing logs.

Replace each of the following words with a more interesting synonym. Use a dictionary or thesaurus to help find the synonyms.
1. run _____
2. good _____
3. brave _____
4. awful _____
5. try _____
6. easy _____
7. walk _____
8. cold _____
9. weak _____

Circle the best expressive word from the three right columns to replace the adjective on the left.
Example: a hot day   blistering   warm   pleasant
1. a high mountain   precipitous   path   level
2. a nice dog   helpful   big   lovable
3. a hungry boy   ravenous   food   fresh
4. a good friend   comforting   helpless   wild
5. a little house   hidden   cozy   magnificent
6. a careful shopper   cautious   important   spendthrift
7. a poor family   hungry   sick   penniless
8. a bad cold   miserable   cured   winter

Using a dictionary or thesaurus, list at least two synonyms for each of the following common words. On the lines below, use one of the synonyms in a sentence.
1. big _____ _____
2. pleased _____ _____
3. hold _____ _____
4. want _____ _____
5. ride _____ _____
6. happy _____ _____
7. eat _____ _____
8. pick _____ _____
9. sing _____ _____
10. smart _____ _____

1. _____
2. _____
3. _____
4. _____
5. _____
6. _____
7. _____
8. _____
9. _____
10. _____

EXTRA!

Select a short paragraph from a book or story you have recently read. Choose three words from the paragraph and write them on a separate sheet of paper. Use a thesaurus to find a more interesting synonym to use in the story. Reread your paragraph with the new words.

Name _____   Date _____

Circle the words that mean the same as the word in boldfaced type from the group below each sentence. Use a **thesaurus** to help choose the **synonyms**.

1. When a knight would leave for the Crusades, each family felt the **anguish** of parting.
   joy   pain   delusion   suffering   poverty

2. Godfrey of Bouillon was given much **latitude** in choosing a route to the Crusades.
   money   freedom   honor   time   help

3. Many of the volunteers who joined the Crusades were **pugnacious** by nature.
   very thin   silly   ready to fight   glad to leave home

4. While the lords of the manor were away at war, many of the fields lay **fallow**.
   tilled   unplanted   fertile   vine-covered   dormant

5. The Crusades were **prolonged** far beyond what had been expected.
   won   shortened   drawn out   finished   enjoyed

Replace the words in boldfaced type with a more exciting descriptive word or words. Rewrite the sentences on the lines.
Example: The knight's armor was **heavy**. The knight's armor was cumbersome.

1. The symbol for the Crusaders was a **big** cross.
   _____

2. Richard the Lion-Hearted was a **good** king.
   _____

3. The Castle-of-the-Sea, a Crusader fortress in the Mediterranean Sea, is quite **old**.
   _____

4. The fate of the Children's Crusade, led by a shepherd boy, was very **sad**.
   _____

5. There were four **main** Crusades between 1096 A.D. and 1204 A.D.
   _____

In the following paragraph, circle the words that mean "trip." Underline the word that means "again and again." Draw two lines under the word that means "told."

Approximately thirty knights and their horses congregated in the courtyard. The horses were restive and stamped their feet repeatedly. The pilgrimage to the Holy Land would begin as soon as the baron bade his wife farewell. The baron appeared and the knights mounted their horses. The clank of armor, the creak of leather, and the rattle of swords were heard as they galloped through the gate. The long journey to Jerusalem had begun.

Look up the word "good" in the thesaurus and write down four of its synonyms. Now write four new sentences, each containing one of the synonyms.

Name _____   Date _____

Harry's hints:
 Synonyms are words that are **similar** in meaning.
 Examples: happy—glad easy—simple huge—enormous
 Antonyms are words that are **opposite** in meaning.
 Examples: hot—cold wonderful—terrible smile—frown

"Am I terribly wonderful?"

Write an **S** if the pair of words are synonyms. Write an **A** if they are antonyms.

___ 1. tired—exhausted   ___ 6. old—antique
___ 2. lose—find   ___ 7. break—fracture
___ 3. clean—dirty   ___ 8. strong—weak
___ 4. cautious—careful   ___ 9. thrifty—stingy
___ 5. drab—colorful   ___ 10. disappointed—delighted

In the blanks below, write an antonym for each word in parentheses.

1. The baseball team arrived (early) _____ at the stadium for the afternoon game.
2. Before the game began the team held a (brief) _____ flag ceremony.
3. The temperature of the playing field was (sweltering) _____ .
4. The game ended after thirteen (exciting) _____ innings.
5. The umpire left the field after a very (easy) _____ game.

In the blanks below, write a synonym for each word in parentheses.

1. The annual dog show, held at Madison Square Garden, was quite (amusing)

_____ .

2. The West Highland terrier (jumped) _____ over the judge's stand.
3. A little beagle (ran) _____ away with his blue ribbon.
4. Several large St. Bernards (pushed) _____ over several spectators' chairs.
5. The judge slipped, fell into the show ring, and felt very (foolish) _____ .

Complete the following rhyming comparisons with an antonym or a synonym from the Word Bank.

WORD BANK	dry	love	sad	down	brave
	slow	tall	cry	win	star

1. Sneaky   is to   sly   as brittle   is to   _____ .
2. Come   ::   go   as fast   :   _____ .
3. Thick   ::   thin   as lose   :   _____ .
4. Near   ::   far   as earth   :   _____ .
5. Push   ::   shove   as like   :   _____ .
6. Little   ::   small   as big   :   _____ .
7. Rescue   ::   save   as bold   :   _____ .
8. Lofty   ::   high   as sob   :   _____ .
9. Subtract ::   add   as happy   :   _____ .
10. Smile   ::   frown   as up   :   _____ .

Homophones are words that **sound alike**, but are **different in spelling and meaning**.
Example: The bridge is made of **steel**. He is trying to **steal** my watch.

In the following sentences, circle any homophones that are used incorrectly. Write the correct word on the line.
Remember: **Their** is a possessive pronoun, **there** is a place, and **they're** is a contraction.

1. They love there new home. _____
2. They're going to move in next Saturday. _____
3. Put the extra boxes over their. _____
4. They're is plenty of room in their new bedrooms. _____
5. The boys must find there clothes to pack. _____
6. Their they are. _____
7. In the new house, they're each going to have a bedroom. _____
8. There going to paint the house white. _____
9. Their goes the moving van. _____
10. They will miss there friends. _____

Write each of the following homophones correctly in a sentence. Use the meaning given in parentheses.

1. rain (precipitation)
_____

2. reign (rule)
_____

3. its (possessive pronoun)
_____

4. it's (contraction of "it is")
_____

5. stationery (writing paper)
_____

6. stationary (not movable)
_____

7. kernel (a seed)
_____

8. colonel (military officer)
_____

9. coarse (large particles)
_____

10. course (part of a meal)
_____

Write a homophone for each of the following words.

1. seen _____   6. won _____   11. cent _____
2. whole _____   7. grown _____   12. aisle _____
3. no _____   8. plane _____   13. he'd _____
4. main _____   9. aloud _____   14. sun _____
5. rode _____   10. flour _____   15. principle _____

Write a paragraph about things that could happen on a trip. Include the homophone that means "to gather sound" and "in this place." Also, use the homophone that is a possessive pronoun and means "in that place."

Harry's hint:
Homophones are words that sound the same, but are spelled differently and have different meanings.

alter/altar	break/brake	feat/feet	principal/principle
capital/capitol	piece/peace	week/weak	stair/stare
rain/reign	here/hear	bored/board	stationary/stationery

Circle the correct word in parentheses:

The morning was very quiet as Tim (threw, through) sticks for his dog to catch. He could (hear/here) barking of other dogs (through, threw) the woods. It was thundering in the distance so he was watching for the (rain, reign) to begin. He took a (piece/peace) of wood and told his dog to leave it at his (feat, feet) until he was told to pick it up. The dog was very well-trained and was told to (stair, stare) at it until Tim gave him a command.

Use each of the following pairs of homophones in a sentence.
Example: weak/week   I felt weak after being in bed a whole week.

break/brake

1. _____
scene/seen

2. _____
bored/board

3. _____
through/threw

4. _____
I/eye

5. _____

Circle the word that answers the following questions.

Which is a story?   tail or tale
Which one is the head of a school?   principle or principal
What has a fragrance?   scent or cent
Which is a part of a window?   pain or pane
Which go to a doctor's appointment?   patients or patience
Which is a piece of fruit?   pear or pair
Which is a meat?   stake or steak

The following sentences are nonsense with the homophones used. Rewrite each sentence correctly.

1. My feat were soar as I tried on my new pear of shoes.

_____

2. Eye eight a peace of caret.

_____

3. Eye have never scene a prettier beech than this won.

_____

4. Hour principle lost his patients over the tail we told.

_____

5. We scent ate students to by to stakes four hour class.

_____

A **conjunction** is a word used to connect words, phrases, and sentences.
Use **and** when the second sentence adds meaning to the first sentence.
Use **but** when the second sentence is in contrast to the first sentence.
Use **or** when there are two choices.

Rewrite each pair of sentences below to make one sentence. Connect them with **and**, **but**, or **or**.
Example: Peter likes to ski. He is very good at it.
Combined: Peter likes to ski**, and** he is very good at it.

1. Peter wanted to ski. There was no snow in England today.

_____

2. He called the tourist office. He asked about snow.

_____

3. Switzerland has plenty of snow. It is far away.

_____

4. Peter could fly to Switzerland. He could save his money for summer vacation.

_____

5. He decided to go at once. He bought a ticket.

_____

Underline the conjunctions in each sentence below. In the blanks, write an **N** if they connect nouns and a **P** if they connect phrases.
__ 1. Ahmud and Larry are on the hockey team.
__ 2. Larry is a skillful player, but a stubborn one.
__ 3. Ahmud has talent and leadership ability.
__ 4. Stubbornness and talent make a winning pair.
__ 5. Ahmud or Larry could become captain of the team.

Connect the words or phrases and use them in a sentence. Choose from these conjunctions:
and, **but**, **or**, **for**, **if**, **nor**, **so**, **when**, **while**, and **yet**.

1. Mary   Jamal   José

_____

2. tall   short

_____

3. ice cream   honey

_____

4. fire   water

_____

5. doctor   ambulance

_____

6. in the river   under a rock

_____

7. into a bucket   out of a pump

_____

8. by train   by plane

_____

In the following sentences, underline the words, phrases, and sentences connected by a conjunction.
1. Oranges grow in California and Florida.
2. Do you want milk or tea?
3. The story was long, but interesting.
4. They played on the beach and in the ocean.
5. She slid down the hill and into a snowbank.
6. The shop sells rings and bracelets.
7. Marie sang and Jerry played the piano.
8. Hal went to the game, but Jay stayed home.
9. The roses grow up and over the fence.
10. The team walked or ran around the track.

70

Name _____   Date _____

A **compound sentence** contains two complete ideas, joined by a **conjunction**.

In the following sentences, underline simple subjects with one line and simple predicates with two lines. On the lines, identify the sentences as either simple or compound sentences. If a sentence is compound, draw a perpendicular line to divide the two sections.

1. The location of Mount St. Helens is fifty miles from Portland, Oregon. _____

2. On March 20, 1980, a seismograph registered an earthquake and recorded the epicenter at Mount St. Helens. _____

3. Seismographs and other equipment were checked and evaluated to pinpoint the exact location of the quake. _____

4. The quake registered 4.1, but that is not considered a major earthquake. _____

5. By March 25, there were forty earthquakes per hour, and this caused geologists to worry about a volcanic eruption. _____

6. On April 1, a state of emergency was called by Governor Dixie Lee Ray, and the United States Forest Service closed roads and access areas. _____

7. The north side of the mountain began to grow and bulge out about five feet a day. _____

8. Clouds and rain prevented scientists from investigating the volcano by air. _____

9. Scientists began to abandon close access areas during the first few days of May, and one geologist, Al Eggers, called for a May 21st eruption of lava. _____

10. Livestock and wildlife acted strangely, and many farmers later told stories about their experiences. _____

11. On May 16, Governor Ray allowed property owners at Spirit Lake several hours to enter the area and recover possessions. _____

12. Harry S. Truman, an 83-year-old Spirit Lake resident, defied the orders to leave the area. _____

Use the conjunctions **and**, **but**, or **either . . . or** to join these sentences or phrases to form compound sentences. Add the necessary capitalization and punctuation.

the explosion on May 18 was heard 200 miles away
a cloud of steam rose 63,000 feet in the air

1. _____
_____

winds were of hurricane force
they blew down millions of two-hundred-year-old trees

2. _____
_____

the forest fires were widespread
the falling ash helped to put out the ensuing fires

3. _____
_____

the temperature of the lahars was 211°F
volcanic mudflows, called lahars, flowed down the mountain at 50 miles per hour

4. _____
_____

everyone realized the ash flowing down the mountain was hot
few realized the temperature was 800 degrees.

5. _____
_____

EXTRA! In 79 B.C.E., on August 24th, a volcano erupted in southern Italy. What was the name of this volcano? Use books or other resources to learn more about this eruption. Write two more compound sentences to provide additional information about this event.

Harry's hints:
   The **subject** tells who or what the sentence is about. It has a **noun** or a **pronoun**.
   The **predicate** tells what the subject is/was; has/had; does/did. The predicate contains the **verb**.

Put a slash mark (/) between the subject and predicate in the following sentences.

1. My family took a trip to Europe last spring.
2. We stayed in many interesting places.
3. My favorite city was London.
4. The art museums proved to be very interesting.
5. The tour guide told us how old the buildings were.

Sometimes the subject does not come first.
Examples: In the thatched roof cottage lived the famous
             author. Through the garden walked the tourists.

Rewrite the sentences below, putting the subject first.

1. Along the sidewalk bloomed the flowers.

   _____

2. By the River Thames painted the artists.

   _____

3. Outside Buckingham Palace stood the guards.

   _____

Add a subject to the following predicates.

1. _____ watched the changing of the guards.
2. _____ sold us roasted chestnuts.
3. _____ was riding in a carriage in Trafalgar Square.

Add a predicate to the following subjects.

1. The royal jewels _____ .
2. Our tour guide _____ .
3. The Tower of London _____ .

Write three sentences about a place you have visited. Put a slash mark (/) between the subject and predicate.

Name _____   Date _____

simple subject
simple predicate

Harry's hints:
    A **simple subject** is the most important word in the subject.
It is a **noun or pronoun**.
    A **simple predicate** is the most important word in the predicate.
It is a **verb**.

Underline the simple subject with one line. Underline the simple predicate with two lines. The simple predicate may have a helping verb.

1. Our class went on a field trip to a farm.
2. The bus left the school promptly at 9:00.
3. The farmer was waiting for us at his barn.
4. First, we saw Guernsey cows in the barnyard.
5. The barn was filled with the smell of fresh hay.
6. The milking machine was very time-efficient.
7. The modern equipment kept the farm working well.
8. In the afternoon we went to the wheat fields.
9. The farmer's wife had baked delicious cookies.
10. The entire family waved good-bye as we left.

The Guernsey breed originated on the Isle of Guernsey in the English Channel off the coast of France.

Use the following nouns and pronouns (simple subjects) and verbs (simple predicates) to write sentences about a trip to a farm.
Underline the simple subject with one line and underline the simple predicate with two lines.

    Simple subjects: sheep, horses, fences, they, she
    Simple verbs: slept, ate, rode, held, worked

1. _____
2. _____
3. _____
4. _____
5. _____

Write a predicate to make a complete sentence. Underline the simple predicate with two lines.
1. The old work horse _____ .
2. The field trip _____ .

Write a subject for each predicate. Underline the simple subject with one line.
1. _____ broke down during the afternoon.
2. _____ was being harvested.

The **subject** of a sentence is the part that **tells who or what** the sentence is about.

In the blanks, indicate whether the subject is a **person, place,** or **thing**.

1. _____ Philip brought books from the library.
2. _____ The library is one of the country's largest.
3. _____ Those books help people to do research.
4. _____ Canada has plenty of frozen ponds.
5. _____ Glennon plays on a hockey team in Canada.
6. _____ The hockey team has a winning record.
7. _____ Tia drove the old car to Florida.
8. _____ Florida has many visitors in the winter.
9. _____ The old car belongs to Salvador's uncle.
10. _____ The lake is a popular place for water skiers.
11. _____ The speedboat was equipped with a large motor.
12. _____ Helen drove the speedboat around the lake.
13. _____ Missouri has many caves.
14. _____ My Aunt Ramona is a spelunker.
15. _____ She has promised to take me caving.

Underline the **simple subject** (the **main noun** or **pronoun** in the subject) in each of the following sentences.

Example: The lovely, bright moonlight shone on the lake.
1. The smell of roasting chestnuts made her hungry.
2. Her visit was cut short.
3. The angry townspeople filled the meeting hall.
4. Ducks swam on the small pond.
5. Where would Pedro go?
6. Happiness is worth the wait.
7. Newspaper headlines told the whole, sad story.
8. The wind scattered leaves all over the yard.
9. Ice on the pond was melting rapidly.
10. The soft light of the moon filtered down through the trees.

Well-chosen modifiers often make the simple subject more interesting. Add at least two adjectives or adjective phrases to the following noun subjects to make **complete subjects**.

Example: **Cheerleaders** practice.   **The energetic cheerleaders for our team** practice daily.

Noun Subject	Modifiers with Subject	Noun Subject	Modifiers with Subject
1. party	_____	6. cake	_____
2. puppy	_____	7. sandwich	_____
3. Hollywood	_____	8. feathers	_____
4. mountain	_____	9. rocket	_____
5. jeep	_____	10. Roberta	_____

In the following Aesop's fable, circle the simple subjects and underline the complete subjects.

A beautiful crystal spring ran through the forest. One day, a large stag stopped for a drink. The clear water showed the stag his reflection. His gracefully arched antlers pleased the stag. But his funny, spindly legs made him ashamed. The unhappy stag wondered why he had such terrible legs on bottom and such magnificence on top.

Suddenly, the strong scent of a panther filled the air. The frightened stag ran into the forest. But his wide-spreading antlers caught in the tree branches. The hungry panther soon overtook him. Then the stag understood. The despised spindly legs would have saved him. But the graceful ornaments on his head were his downfall.

Subjects that share the same verb or verbs are **compound subjects**.
Example: **Kevin** and **Paula** play basketball.

Fill in the following blanks so that each sentence has a compound subject.

1. _____ and _____ took turns at the video game.
2. This _____ and that _____ are good friends.
3. _____ and Malcolm brought plenty of groceries.
4. Where are _____ and _____?
5. _____ and _____ built a huge tree house.
6. _____ and _____ barked at the postal carrier.
7. Mice and _____ are very small.
8. _____ and Franklin will help fix dinner.
9. Why can't _____ and _____ go on the trip?
10. _____ and _____ are my favorite subjects in school.

Verbs that share the same subject or subjects are **compound predicates**.
Example: Two class members will **go** and **report** on the speaker.

Next to the following nouns, fill in two verbs that could make compound predicates.

1. actor _____ _____
2. teachers _____ _____
3. race cars _____ _____
4. storm _____ _____
5. snakes _____ _____

6. Jane _____ _____
7. grass _____ _____
8. river _____ _____
9. police officer _____ _____
10. eagle _____ _____

Compound sentences are two simple sentences joined by a connector. The new sentence contains two **independent clauses**.
Example: The weather was warm. It was breezy.
Connected: The weather was warm**, and** it was breezy.

In the blanks, write an independent clause and a connector to make a compound sentence.

1. _____ Jake's bike is faster than mine.
2. _____ I could not find the belt.
3. _____ Kelly likes to fix mechanical things.
4. _____ cars often break down on that road.
5. _____ Frances likes to read novels.
6. _____ the FBI agent saw the spy.
7. _____ the hills were covered with snow.
8. _____ Su Yung is usually warm.
9. _____ Patricia is a whiz at math.
10. _____ Florida is a peninsula.

Write a paragraph about an imaginary trip to Mars. Include two sentences with compound subjects, three sentences with compound predicates, and four compound sentences.

_____
_____
_____
_____
_____
_____
_____
_____
_____
_____

A **clause** is part of a sentence containing a **subject and a predicate**. An **adjective clause** usually begins with **who**, **which**, or **that**. It can begin with **when**, **where**, or **why** if it is used to modify a noun or pronoun.

Underline only the adjective clauses in the phrases below. In the blanks, write the word each clause modifies.

_____ 1. the girl who lives on High Street
_____ 2. the dancers in their colorful costumes
_____ 3. the zoo where they saw the panda
_____ 4. the new president whom everybody cheered
_____ 5. the little boy on a swing
_____ 6. the old couch that I finally repaired
_____ 7. the movie that Jane wanted to see
_____ 8. the sweater in the store window
_____ 9. the band that Jose brought to the studio
_____ 10. the bridge over the swollen river

On the lines below, write the numeral of the group of words that could be used to make an adverbial clause. Example: 11. after two months _11_ had passed

1. before the train	__ chewed on a bone
2. after she	__ picked a team
3. because Trina	__ counted votes
4. when the door	__ crossed the bridge
5. while the dog	__ had tears in her eyes
6. while Angelina	__ slammed shut
7. because Juanita	__ pressed her skirt
8. before the coach	__ was ready first

Choose five of the completed clauses above and write a sentence for each one.

1. _____
2. _____
3. _____
4. _____
5. _____

Independent clauses could stand alone and could be punctuated as sentences. They remain independent, even though they are connected by a conjunction. Only independent clauses that are **related in meaning** should be connected.
Example: The month for the class reunion came, and all the members were excited. (These clauses are related in meaning.)

Connect the following sentences to a related independent clause. Use **and**, **or**, **but**, or **yet** as connectors.

1. The swimmers took extra towels _____
2. He turned on the television _____
3. Snow was falling _____
4. The car slid _____
5. The zoo gates closed at 5:00 _____
6. Today has been the hottest of the year _____

EXTRA!

Write four of your own examples of sentences containing independent clauses.
Use **and**, **or**, **but**, and **yet** as a connector at least once.

Harry's hints:
 A **sentence** is a group of words that makes sense.
It must have a subject and a predicate.
Examples: I love ice hockey. Do you enjoy skating?
 A **fragment** does not have both parts of a sentence.
Examples: skate at the rink   the players on the team

Put **S** before each sentence. Put **F** before each fragment.

1. ____ Steven is a good goalie.

2. ____ hurt my leg

3. ____ among the spectators

4. ____ with a penalty

5. ____ stops the puck

6. ____ I played the whole game.

7. ____ My parents were watching.

8. ____ The team lost control of the puck.

Rewrite one of the fragments as a complete sentence by adding a subject or predicate part.

_____

Harry's hint:
 A **run-on sentence** has too many thoughts.
Example: Ice hockey is played in three periods my brother is the goalie.
 These thoughts should be separated into separate sentences.
Example: Ice hockey is played in three periods. My brother is the goalie.

Write the following run-on sentences as two separate sentences. Use proper punctuation and capitalization.

1. The lineman was put into the penalty box for fighting he was very angry. _____

_____

2. The machine that makes the ice on the rink was brought on because the ice was melting it was a very warm day. _____

_____

3. We decided to stay for the whole game it was a very long game due to many fights and penalties. _____

_____

Use the proofreading marks in the box to correct the paragraph below.

delete	make a capital	make lowercase	make a period
—℮	=	/	⊙

 Ice hockey is a popular sport played around the world in Canada The game began in the early 1900s. In order to keep the game moving quickly, players are substituted while the game is in progress the action can include fights among players. The players need to be very good skaters the games are played. In three 20-minute periods.

Name _____ Date _____

Some of the following groups of words are sentences; some are not. Put **S** for a **sentence** and **F** for a **fragment**. Underline all action verbs.

1. ___ The Greeks fought many great wars.
2. ___ At the top of Mount Olympus.
3. ___ Large forests cover the mountain tops.
4. ___ The difference between ancient and modern Greece.
5. ___ Farmers plow their small fields.
6. ___ Almost five hundred years ago.
7. ___ The island in the Mediterranean Sea.
8. ___ The Greeks constantly travel by boat.
9. ___ Zeus ruled the mythical gods.
10. ___ The white sandy beach.

In the space after each number, write an **A** for an **action verb** and a **B** for a **verb of being**. Write a sentence for each of the verbs of being.

1. ___ ran   6. ___ sailed   11. ___ am
2. ___ was   7. ___ were   12. ___ hit
3. ___ got   8. ___ told   13. ___ fought
4. ___ became   9. ___ is   14. ___ lifts
5. ___ shouted   10. ___ seemed   15. ___ are

_____
_____
_____
_____
_____
_____
_____
_____

Draw a line under the verb in parentheses that makes the paragraph more interesting.

Medusa, once a beautiful woman, was (turned, transformed) into an ugly monster. Snakes (writhed, lay) on her head in place of hair. Her fingers (grew, stretched) into claws of bronze. Anyone who dared to (stare, look) into her eyes immediately turned to stone. The mythical hero, Perseus, (fooled, outwitted) her by looking at a reflection in a mirror instead of directly into her face. Perseus (cut, slashed) off the monster's head. Medusa (crashed, fell) to her death.

Fill in the blanks in the sentences below with either a verb of being or an action verb as directed in the parentheses.

(Being) 1. Jason _____ the leader of the Argonauts.

(Action) 2. Jason and his men _____ the great ship Argo.

(Action) 3. They _____ to find the golden fleece so Jason could inherit his uncle's throne.

(Action) 4. After many adventures, Jason _____ the golden fleece and escaped with it.

(Being) 5. In his old age, Jason's home _____ near the beach where the rotting Argo lay.

Pin the verb on the sentence

hate

I ____ ICE CREAM

like

crave   ate

Harry's hints:
     A **declarative** sentence makes a statement.
Example: John's birthday party is today.
     An **interrogative** sentence asks a question.
Example: Who will be there?
     An **imperative** sentence gives a command or makes a request.
A command is more demanding. Example: Climb down from that chandelier!
A request is softer in nature. Example: Please bring me some cake.
     An **exclamatory** sentence shows strong feeling or surprise.
Examples: Goodness! What a party!

Identify the type of sentence by writing declarative, imperative, interrogative, or exclamatory to the right of the sentence.

1. John had a surprise birthday party today. _____

2. Did you receive an invitation? _____

3. You should have seen the birthday cake! _____

4. It was a foot high! _____

5. Please write his mother a thank-you note. _____

6. Stop feeding birthday cake to the dog. _____

7. Did you play many games? _____

8. John received many books, games, and puzzles. _____

9. Was he really surprised or did he know about the party? _____

10. It was the best birthday party ever! _____

> Sometimes, in a command or a request, the subject is **you**, but it is not written.
> Examples: (You) Close the door! Sam, (you) bring the ice cream.

Write three imperative sentences using the unwritten "you" as the subject.

1. _____
2. _____
3. _____

Write four sentences about a birthday party. Use one of each type of sentence: declarative, imperative, interrogative, and exclamatory.

1. _____
2. _____
3. _____
4. _____

Name _____   Date _____

To make sentences more interesting, the subject and predicate are sometimes written in **reverse order**.
Example: John stood next to the car. (natural order)
        Next to the car stood John. (reverse order)

In each of the following sentences, circle the verb and place an **N** in front of natural order sentences and an **R** in front of reverse order sentences.

___ 1. Sarah looked at the stars through a telescope.
___ 2. Beside the garage stood a large doghouse.
___ 3. In what city is the Liberty Bell?
___ 4. The dog lay in front of the fire.
___ 5. In the front seat sat the driving instructor.
___ 6. Lavell kept the best jewelry in the top drawer.
___ 7. Under what bridge does the river flow?
___ 8. Eleanor looked in the refrigerator for juice.
___ 9. The doctor has a large waiting room.
___ 10. Next to its post rested the broken mailbox.

A **direct object** is a noun or pronoun that receives the action of the verb.
Example: The ball hit the **glove** right in the center. ("Glove" receives the action of the verb "hit".)

Underline the direct object in each of the following sentences.

1. The detective followed the suspect.
2. The big dog sniffed the tracks.
3. The snow quickly covered the footprints.
4. A scarf on the path made a good clue.
5. He turned the corner.
6. A thick hedge blocked his view.
7. He heard the noise of running feet.
8. He pulled his coat tighter.
9. Then he began the chase.
10. The detective reached the suspect just in time.

A **predicate nominative** is a noun or pronoun that follows a linking verb. It denotes the same person or thing as the subject.
Example: The clue was a plaid wool **scarf**. (The scarf is the same thing as the clue.)

Complete the following sentences by adding a predicate nominative.

1. Porpoises are _____
2. My aunt will soon be _____
3. Knives can be _____
4. At last Alan has become _____
5. After five months of training, Rita will be _____
6. Airline pilots are _____
7. The morning was _____
8. A man in a blue uniform will be _____
9. This book of poetry has become _____
10. The shimmering lake is _____

In each sentence in the following Aesop's fable, underline the complete predicate and circle any direct object.

A large pitcher filled with delicious nuts stood on the kitchen table. The bottom of the pitcher was wide, but the top was narrow. The boy who lived in the house asked his mother for some nuts. She nodded her head. He took an extra large fistful. He was not able to get his hand out of the narrow top. The boy began to cry.

His mother came to the rescue. She told him to be satisfied with half of the nuts he had grabbed. Then he could pull his hand out again. And he could get more nuts later.

A **topic sentence** states the **main idea** of a paragraph.

Underline any sentence below that could be a topic sentence.

1. The automobile show is entertaining and informative.
2. Crowds pushed harder and harder.
3. Christmas is a special time of year.
4. It is funny and sad too.
5. Where did he go?
6. The cast met in the gymnasium for play practice.

Write a topic sentence for each pair of sentences below.

Topic sentence: _____
First, Gary put on his hockey skates. Then he tightened the laces.

Topic sentence: _____
Carlos sharpened his blue pencil. After that he got out his notebook.

Topic sentence: _____
Dark clouds gathered overhead. Thunder rumbled and lightning flashed.

Add two sentences relating to each topic sentence below.

James set aside Saturday afternoon to repair his bicycle. _____

_____

_____

_____

When it was time to paint the school bus, the entire class decided to help in two ways. _____

_____

_____

_____

The grassy spot overlooking the lake made a wonderful campsite. _____

_____

_____

_____

In the paragraph below, cross out any sentences that do not relate to the topic sentence.

Maria loved to help her father, a baker, make bread. She mixed the ingredients while her father prepared the baking pans. Then together the two of them kneaded the dough. A bright blue rag rug covered the kitchen floor. Very carefully Maria fitted a mound of dough into a pan and put it in the oven. A wonderful smell filled the kitchen as the bread began to bake. The sun shone brightly through the window. The birds were singing outside. The best part of the baking was eating the homemade bread.

Sentences in a paragraph should follow the topic sentence in **sequential order**.

The sentences in the paragraph below are in sequential order. The words in boldfaced type are clues to the sequence.

The Great Wall of China is a well-known landmark. It was built during **the third century B.C.** The Wall was **originally** constructed as a defense against wandering tribes. **Later** the Wall was lengthened. **Now** it is 1500 miles long. **Today** visitors are impressed with this wonderful monument to the past.

Rewrite the sentences below in sequential order. Begin with the topic sentence. Underline the words that give clues to the sequence.

1. Then they are allowed to sit on the floor and read.
2. One type is a small shop that sells food and bright, colored cards.
3. The streets of many large cities in China are lined with shops.
4. In addition, the shop is a library.
5. First, customers pay the shopkeeper a small amount of money.

1. _____
2. _____
3. _____
4. _____
5. _____

Write a short paragraph about the following topic sentence. Clues have been furnished to help plan the order of the sentences.

My birthday is always special for me.

First, _____

Then _____

Afterwards, _____

Finally _____

Using the following topic sentences, write three sentences in sequential order for each one.

The school day is busy for me.

_____

_____

_____

I have tried to take good photographs.

_____

_____

_____

Spring is my favorite season for several reasons.

_____

_____

_____

EXTRA! Reread the paragraph about China at the top of the page. Find at least one synonym for each sequence clue in boldfaced type. Rewrite the paragraph using your synonyms. Use a thesaurus to help you.

There are at least three steps to help you write a clear **definition** of a word. The first is to decide its general **classification**.

Example: A **bicycle** is a means of **transportation**.

Add the general classification to each of the following nouns.

1. brick house _____
2. video camera _____
3. tennis shoes _____
4. rose _____
5. tea _____
6. wrist watch _____
7. poetry book _____
8. bobsled _____

A second step in writing clear definitions is to describe how an object is **different from** others in its classification.

Example: A **bicycle** has two large wheels, a seat, handlebars, brakes, but it usually has **no motor**.

Write a sentence for each of the eight nouns above and describe how each is different from all the others in its class.

1. _____
2. _____
3. _____
4. _____
5. _____
6. _____
7. _____
8. _____

A third step in writing a clear definition is to explain the object's **function**, or how it is used.

Example: Many students find a **bicycle** a simple **way to travel** from home to school.

For each of the above nouns, add another sentence explaining the function or use of each.

1. _____
2. _____
3. _____
4. _____
5. _____
6. _____
7. _____
8. _____

Using the three steps above, write a clear, concise definition for each of the following nouns: pizza, fork, jet plane, cow.

1. _____
_____
_____

2. _____
_____
_____

3. _____
_____
_____

4. _____
_____
_____

Rearrange the parts of a **friendly letter** to be in the proper position. Use correct capitalization and punctuation. You do not need to write the body of the letter. Follow the example for the correct form.

HEADING:
                                        20 Marine Drive
                                        Orlando, Florida 32802
                                        August 10, 1989

GREETING: Dear Charlie,

                    BODY of letter

CLOSING: Your friend,

SIGNATURE: Hal

1. lots of luck   dear tim   march 17 1990   lawrence kansas 66044   254 deer creek road   john

_____
_____
_____
_____
_____
_____
_____
_____
_____
_____

2. dear holly   love   marie   1257 martinville street   lima ohio 45804   may 3 1995

_____
_____
_____
_____
_____
_____
_____
_____
_____

EXTRA! Pretend that someone in your class has won an award. On a separate sheet of paper, write a friendly letter of congratulations to him or her. Be warm and honest.

Main topics in an outline are identified with **Roman numerals**.
Subtopics are identified with **capital letters**.
Further details are identified with **Arabic numerals**.
Use a **capital letter** to begin each division.

Title
I. Topic
    A. Subtopic
        1. Further detail
        2. Further detail
    B. Subtopic
        1. Further detail
        2. Further detail

Rewrite the outline below. Use correct identification, capitalization, and punctuation.

    learning to play the piano   _____
early skills   _____
    learning to read notes   _____
    practicing scales   _____
        major scales   _____
        minor scales   _____
intermediate skills   _____
    learning tempo   _____
    how to use a metronome   _____
    learning fingering   _____
advanced skills   _____
    interpretation   _____
    styles of different composers   _____
        classical   _____
        modern   _____

Listed below are several topics and subtopics. Unscramble them and put them in proper outline form.

sports   _____
volleyball   _____
football   _____
chess   _____
team sports   _____
tennis   _____
baseball   _____
soccer   _____
golf   _____
Ping-Pong   _____
one or two player sports   _____

Harry's hints:
When you fill out forms, follow several rules:
Read through the entire form first.
Think carefully about what you plan to write.
Practice on a separate piece of paper first.
Write neatly and carefully on the lines.

MAIL ORDER FORMS

Choose two items from the following excerpt from The Starr Mail Order Catalog. Follow the directions to order, fill out the form carefully, and add your purchases. Be sure to add the shipping charges.

#6498 Kaleidoscopes
1 Set $6.98 2 Sets
$12.98

#7112 Globe Puzzle
Colorful sphere of
29 pieces. $11.98

#8502 2 Giant Dinosaurs
Realistic models of
prehistoric animals. 1 Set
$8.98. 2 Sets $16.98

Item Number*******	Quantity***	Name of Item***	Price Each**	Total Price
#				

Shipping Charges:
Up to $20, add $3.25
$20.01–$35, add $4.25
$35.01–$50, add $5.25

Merchandise Total	
Shipping Charges	
Order Total	

You might pay for your order with a personal check. You must follow certain rules to fill out the check. Write the correct date. On the second line, "Pay to the Order of," write The Starr Mail Order Company. After the dollar sign, fill in the Order Total. (see above) The next line is a safeguard because the dollar amount is written out. Example: Seven dollars and ----------------- 45/100 Your signature is written on the last line.

No. 432

_____
(date)

Pay to the Order of _____ $ _____
                   (name of company)

_____ Dollars
(amount written out)

_____
(your signature)

Harry's hints:

A diamante is a seven-line, unrhymed poem. Its name comes from an Italian word that means diamond-shaped, the form the poem takes on paper.

Dawn
Pink, orange
Awakening, stretching, yawning
A brand new day
Showering, dressing, eating
Bright, fresh
Morning

"They call me a diamond in the ruff."

A diamante may be written as the sample above, using synonyms for the first and last lines. Follow the rules to write a diamante on the lines below.

Line 1—one topic word
Line 2—two adjectives describing the topic word
Line 3—three action verbs or participles
Line 4—a four-word phrase showing feeling about the topic
Line 5—three action verbs or participles
Line 6—two adjectives describing the topic word
Line 7—a synonym for the topic word

_____

_____

_____

_____

_____

_____

_____

Write a diamante using antonyms. It will be easier to write if you follow these rules in this order:

Line 1—one topic word
Line 7—an antonym for the topic word
Line 2—two adjectives describing the topic word
Line 6—two adjectives describing the antonym
Line 3—three action verbs or participles for the topic word
Line 5—three action verbs or participles for the antonym
Line 4—two adjectives about the topic word; then two adjectives about the antonym

_____

_____

_____

_____

_____

_____

_____

EXTRA!

Draw an illustration for your favorite diamante and share your poem and picture with a friend.

Name _____   Date _____

You can apply skills you have learned to enjoy and understand interesting things in literature.

Read the following poem by John Masefield and answer the questions.

Cargoes

Quinquireme of Nineveh from distant Ophir
Rowing home to haven in sunny Palestine,
With a cargo of ivory,
And apes and peacocks,
Sandalwood, cedarwood, and sweet white wine.

Stately Spanish galleon coming from the Isthmus,
Dipping through the Tropics by the palm-green shores,
With a cargo of diamonds,
Emeralds, amethysts,
Topazes, and cinnamon, and gold moidores.

Dirty British coaster with a salt-caked smoke stack
Butting through the Channel in the mad March days
With a cargo of Tyne coal,
Road-rail, pig-lead,
Firewood, iron-ware, and cheap tin trays.

Answer the following questions about John Masefield's poem.
1. How many stanzas are there in the poem? _____
2. What concrete thing do you think each stanza represents? _____
3. In the first stanza, how is the ship propelled? _____
4. How is the first cargo different from the last? _____
_____
5. Which words in the first stanza rhyme? _____
    second stanza? _____
    third stanza? _____
6. What channel is being referred to in the third stanza? _____
7. Look up the definitions of the following words and write them down:
cargo _____
haven _____
galleon _____
amethyst _____
sandalwood _____
isthmus _____

Add a fourth stanza to the poem. Make it as similar as you can to John Masefield's poem.
Follow this pattern:

    The first line tells about a certain kind of ship.
    The second line tells where the ship is sailing.
    The third, fourth, and fifth lines describe the cargo.
    The second and fifth lines rhyme.

_____
_____
_____
_____
_____

MP5093 - Grammar   **88**   Composition Types

Use newspaper headlines to help generate ideas for writing.

The following newspaper headlines are possible ideas for parts of a story. Put **M** in front of those that could be about a **main character**, **P** for those that could be about a **problem** discussed in the story, or **S** for those that could be the **solution** to the problem.

1. ___ Fourteen-year-old Breaks Skating Record
2. ___ Fire Roars Through Old Building
3. ___ Police Puzzled Over Disappearance of Antique Car
4. ___ Why Has Mayor Clay Left Town?
5. ___ Australian Girl Meets American Cousins
6. ___ Bridge Buckles After Storm
7. ___ Bank Robber Given Stiff Sentence
8. ___ Dog Rescues Child from Pond
9. ___ Plane Crashes in the Rockies
10. ___ Astronauts to Arrive Monday

Write three fictitious headlines about a person. Begin the first word and each important word with a capital letter.

1. _____
2. _____
3. _____

Write three fictitious headlines about a problem.

1. _____
2. _____
3. _____

Write three fictitious headlines about the solution to a problem.

1. _____
2. _____
3. _____

Choose either a fictitious character, problem, or solution from the headlines you wrote above to use as the basis for a short story. Include the characters, setting, problem, and the solution to the problem in your story.

_____
_____
_____
_____
_____
_____
_____
_____
_____
_____

Harry's favorite feat is telling jokes. He makes all his friends laugh.

We all need to tell about our best accomplishments, our greatest "feats," from time to time. This project is to tell about your greatest feat and write it on the pattern to the right.

Think about what activities you enjoy and what you do the best. Perhaps you make the best chocolate cookie in your neighborhood, or maybe you are the fastest runner in your school. Think of one special "feat" of which you are proud.

Use the outline below to plan your story.

My Greatest Feat

My greatest feat is _____

_____

for two reasons.

First, _____

_____ .

* _____

(Add a supporting sentence.)

_____ .

Second, _____

_____ .

* _____

(Add a supporting sentence.)

_____ .

Edit and proofread your paragraph. Copy it over on the foot at the right and cut it out. Collect your friends' "feats" and make a booklet by joining the pages together with a ring clip at the top.

Name _____ Date _____

Harry's hints:
Use a **capital letter** to begin:
    a sentence,
    all proper names,
    the first word in a direct quotation,
    the pronoun I,
    a title of respect,
    the first word and all important words in a book title,
    the first word in the greeting and in the closing of a letter,
    the first word in a line of poetry.

harry hound
(≡ make a capital)

Use the proofreading mark to show where capital letters are needed in the following phrases and sentences.

1. jenny perkins lives at 228 matthew street.
2. tuesday, february 7, 1989, is the correct date.
3. my brother and i went to the united states post office.
4. halloween and thanksgiving are both in the fall.
5. charlotte's web was written by e. b. white.
6. doctor john burns is my dentist.
7. new york city, new york, is where the convention is held.
8. carol cobb cookie company advertises in the county journal.
9. dear mrs. daly,
10. "come to my house," said annalise.

Use the proofreading mark to indicate where capital letters are needed in these limericks.

there once was a girl named joan
who talked all day on the phone.
    her bill was high
    but she gave a sigh
and called bay bank for a loan.

there once was a hound named harry
who thought halloween was scary.
    he went out that night
    as a frightful sight
just dressed as his twin larry.

Advertisements in newspapers need to be proofread before they are printed. Use the proofreading mark to indicate where capital letters are needed.

garage sale
september 7, 1989
976 woodgate ave.

house for sale
open house
wednesday 10:00
1414 tappan lane
cincinnati, ohio

valentine's day
party
los angeles city hall
february 14, 1990

Pretend you own a company that manufactures something to sell to the public. Give your company and the product special names. Then create an advertisement for your product and illustrate it on a separate sheet of paper.

Capitalize **proper names** and **titles**. Titles that are abbreviated are followed by a period. Capitalize common nouns that become part of a proper name. An initial is a capital letter followed by a period.

The sixth grade class of Elm Grove School is presenting an original drama for the entire school, staff, and parents. The following list of characters will be printed on the program. Rewrite the names on the lines at the right, making any necessary corrections.

The Players
(in order of appearance)

1. doctor r j stone _____
2. reverend hollister _____
3. policeman _____
4. captain cook _____
5. governor harold blake _____
6. mr. larry t hill _____
7. mrs. mary haas _____
8. professor judd _____
9. grocer _____
10. aunt maggie _____
11. ms helen tucker _____
12. little girl _____
13. uncle harry _____
14. miss whitman _____
15. major collins _____

Following the performance, these notes for the cast were displayed on the drama room bulletin board. Some of the letters are missing. Write a capital or lowercase letter in each blank.

___rank, congratulations on your portrayal of the ___overnor!
___uzie

___ob,
    Although it is hard for me to picture you as a minister, you did a fine job as the ___everend.
___amantha

___anice, I am so proud that you are my friend. You were just great as the ___unt.
___ina

___eorge:
    You were the best ___ncle ___arry ever! Maybe you should try out for ___racula next!
___arvin

Dear ___oan,
    You were marvelous as the little ___irl. You will be a famous ___ctress someday.
___athy

Dear ___iss ___mith,
    Thanks for being such a marvelous and patient drama teacher.
Love,
The Cast

Design a poster that advertises the school's play. Choose a title for the play, and be sure to include the names of the main characters and the location of the performance. Capitalize all proper names and titles.

A **comma** is used to separate words and phrases in a series. The last comma is followed by **and**.

Example: We traveled to Turkey, Pakistan, **and** India.

⌃, add
a
comma

Use the proofreading mark to show where commas are needed in the following sentences:

1. India is famous for elephants tea and the Taj Mahal.
2. The Taj Mahal is a beautiful tomb built with a double dome a very high entrance portal and four corner domes.
3. The building features white marble red sandstone and a lovely garden.
4. The huge monument is decorated with jewels alabaster screens and carved writings from the Koran.
5. Around the outside are four towers or minarets a lovely reflecting pool and a peaceful river.

Write a sentence for each series of words below.

1. house hill history

_____

2. wood steel metal

_____

3. Marie Sally Louise

_____

4. bicycle automobile trucks

_____

5. river mountain city

_____

Choose three words from the WORD BOX to match each numbered category. Write and punctuate each series correctly.

WORD BOX	meat	books	wolves	tires	drums	microphone	brakes	eggs
	geese	potatoes	desk	fox	guitars	headlights	teacher	

1. dinner _____   4. automobile _____
2. school _____   5. concert _____
3. Aesop fable _____

Write a correctly punctuated series of words to answer each question.

1. What are four girls' names?

_____

2. What are the names of three holidays?

_____

3. What are the seasons of the year?

_____

4. What are the names of the four inner planets?

_____

5. What are the names of three national monuments?

_____

Name _____   Date _____

⌃, add a comma

Use a **comma**:
A. to separate a series of three or more items;
     (bread, butter, and jelly)
B. to separate parts of a compound sentence or set off clauses;
     (We were planning a visit, but we didn't know her address.)
C. to set off appositives and nouns of direct address;
     (Stacy, my friend, is here. Tina, will you sit down please?)
D. to separate introductory words and interrupters.
     (No, I don't believe it! To tell the truth, I didn't see it.)

Use the proofreading mark to add the missing commas in these sentences. Put the letter of the rule(s) you followed in the parentheses.

1. ( ) Serena Crisp my friend is a spelunker.
2. ( ) Actually she is a spelunker and a speologist.
3. ( ) If you investigate a cave for a scientific reason you are a speologist.
4. ( ) A speologist investigates caves in winter spring summer and fall.
5. ( ) Caving I believe is a very physical activity.
6. ( ) To explore a cave requires many tools much patience and a lot of courage.
7. ( ) ( ) When Serena enters a cave she has three sources of light a hard hat and sturdy boots.
8. ( ) She often takes friends caving but she makes sure they are well prepared.
9. ( ) You can take a boat ride explore a tunnel or see unusual stone shapes in Mammoth Cave.
10. ( ) Carlsbad Caverns a cave in New Mexico is the largest cave in the United States.
11. ( ) Names based on the formations include the Throne Room in Wyandotte Cavern the Parachute in Lehman Cave and the Christmas Tree in Carlsbad Caverns.
12. ( ) Missouri the "cave state" has nearly 5,000 caves.
13. ( ) Cave dwellers include bats cave fish and spiders.
14. ( ) Serena will you take me spelunking?

Use these series of words in sentences. Be sure to include commas.

1. bats water and mud

  _____

2. stalagmites stalactites and columns

  _____

3. brown furry bats

  _____

4. through the clay under the water and over the rocks

  _____

Write a short paragraph on the topic of your choice. In your paragraph, include each of the comma examples above at least once.

Harry's hints:
Quotation marks are used to show conversation or direct quotations.
A **comma** is used to separate the **speaker tag** from the quotation.

Example A: Libby asked, "Are you ready for the ballet?"

Example B: "I am almost ready to go," replied Joannna.

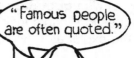
"Famous people are often quoted."

Use the following speaker tags to write six sentences with quotation marks. Write three sentences like Example A above, in which the speaker tag comes first. Write three sentences like Example B, in which the speaker tag appears at the end of the quotation.

| she asked | he whispered | Andrea replied |
| Michael shouted | she complained | Meg shrieked |

1. _____
2. _____
3. _____
4. _____
5. _____
6. _____

Roosevelt

Franklin

Kennedy

Twain

Correctly punctuate the following famous quotations:

1. And so, my fellow Americans, ask not what your country can do for you, but what you can do for your country said John F. Kennedy in his Inaugural Address in 1961.

2. President Franklin D. Roosevelt exclaimed as the United States entered World War II The only thing we have to fear is fear itself

3. Early to bed and early to rise, makes a man healthy, wealthy, and wise wrote Benjamin Franklin in <u>Poor Richard's Almanac</u>.

4. Neil Armstrong radioed from the moon in July, 1969 Houston, Tranquility Base here. The Eagle has landed

Pretend you are asked to give advice to a new student in your school. Write down your advice to this student. Be sure to use correct punctuation marks.

Use **quotation marks** at the beginning and end of a direct quotation. Put exclamation points and question marks inside the quotation marks if they belong with the quotation. Use commas to set off the explanatory words.

Rewrite this joke as a direct quote.

Two strawberries were walking down the street. One strawberry told the other that if it wasn't for him, they wouldn't be in this jam.

_____

Rewrite this story about a man in Alaska. Add the necessary quotation marks and other punctuation marks. Use capital letters where necessary.

1. do you feel well asked his wife

_____

2. yes i am fine why he replied

_____

3. well she said you look as though your skin is turning orange

_____

4. orange he exclaimed are you kidding

_____

5. say you are right i do look orange he laughed

_____

6. perhaps he told his wife living in alaska for three years has done this maybe i am not getting enough sun

_____

_____

7. the man went to see his doctor doctor he said i seem to be turning orange do you have any advice

_____

_____

8. tell me about your diet are you getting enough vitamins questioned the doctor

_____

_____

9. well he replied i eat a lot of carrots and yellow vegetables and i drink a lot of tomato juice

_____

_____

10. i know what is wrong said the doctor you are eating too many yellow orange and red foods stop eating those foods and you will turn back to your normal color

_____

_____

_____

EXTRA! If you could have a conversation with anyone in history, to whom would you speak? What would you say? Write a short conversation between you and the person of your choice. Be sure to use quotation marks correctly.

Quotation marks are used around the title of a story, poem, article, or chapter in a book.

In the following sentences, place quotation marks around the proper group of words.

1. How the Elephant Got His Trunk is an amusing story.
2. *Sports Illustrated* had a good article called How to Hit a Homerun.
3. Where Was the Key? is the most exciting chapter in the book.
4. Mrs. Street made the poem, The Song of Hiawatha, sound interesting.

Pretend that your teacher has given you a research assignment on the topic of music in the '80's. List titles of imaginary resources you might use.
Example: Magazine article—"Bruce: Still the Boss"

1. Story: _____
2. Magazine article: _____
3. Musicians' report: _____
4. Chapter from performing arts book: _____
5. Chapter from a biography: _____

Circle the letter under YES if quotation marks are used correctly in the sentence. Circle the letter under NO if they are not. Write the letter circled above the matching numeral to spell the name of a famous poem by Robert Frost.

YES	NO
I	L
R	C
N	B
E	W
A	H
O	R
S	T

1. "The Gift of the Magi" is a story from O. Henry's *Book of Short Stories*.
2. "A Tale of Two Cities" is a book about the French Revolution.
3. At "Macy's Department Store" there are many good stories, like "Peter Pan," in the book department.
4. The poem "Where the Sidewalk Ends" is in a collection by Shel Silverstein.
5. "The Encyclopedia of Dinosaurs" is much bigger than the story "Digging Up Dinosaurs."
6. The article by "Claire Daley" was fascinating for amateur photographers.
7. "My Last Seven Minutes" was the scariest chapter in the whole book.

"__ __ __ __ __ __ __"
  3   1   6   2   5   4   7

List three stories and three poems you like. Place quotation marks where they are needed.

Stories: _____
_____
_____

Poems: _____
_____
_____

Capitalize the first word and all the important words in a **book title**. Underline a book title when it appears in a sentence.

Paul has made a list of some of his class' favorite books. Rewrite the titles and correct any capitalization mistakes.

1. henry Reed's baby-sitting Service _____
2. the call Of the wild _____
3. jamie and the Mystery quilt _____
4. A tale of Two Cities _____
5. johnny tremaine _____
6. the Legend Of sleepy hollow _____
7. The secret garden _____
8. tales of Mystery and imagination _____
9. the diary of a young Girl _____
10. North To the orient _____

Name four books that you like:

_____ _____
_____ _____

Capitalize the first word and all the important words in a **magazine title**. Rewrite these magazine titles if needed:

1. Seventeen _____
2. RANGER RICK _____
3. readers' Digest _____
4. sports illustrated _____
5. natural HISTORY magazine _____

Choose one of the magazines named above and list three feature articles that might be found in that publication. Put quotation marks around the names of the **magazine articles**.

Magazine Title: _____ Article 2: _____

Article 1: _____ Article 3: _____

Capitalize the first word and all the important words in the names of **plays and movies**. Rewrite these names if needed.

1. cats _____
2. the Taming of The shrew _____
3. the sound of music _____
4. fiddler on the Roof _____
5. arsenic and old Lace _____

EXTRA! Write the titles of your favorite **songs**. Capitalize the first word and all other important words.

Name _____   Date _____

List the books below in alphabetical order by the author's last name. Use the correct capitalization, punctuation, and form for a **bibliography**.
Example: Stevenson, Robert Lewis. Kidnapped.

mary queen of scots by antonia fraser
great true spy stories by allen dulles
the lamp lighters by marguerite vance
the owl's nest by dorothy glady spicer
hard times by charles dickens

1. _____

2. _____

3. _____

4. _____

5. _____

Bibliographies may contain more explicit information. Study the following example and then write the given information in proper form.

Example: Fraser, Antonia. Mary Queen of Scots, a Biography. England: Weidenfeld & Nicolson, 1969.

Book 1. the old trevor farm   new york   1982   wilton press   harry sullivan
Book 2. under sail   richard hill   1978   boston   oldtimer publications
Book 3. mary delaney walters   1900   the country garden   london   druid publishers

1. _____

_____

2. _____

_____

3. _____

_____

Select three books on the subject of tennis or other sport. Choose from your school or local library. Prepare a complete bibliography of the books chosen.

Subject _____

Book 1. _____

_____

Book 2. _____

_____

Book 3. _____

_____

Name _____   Date _____

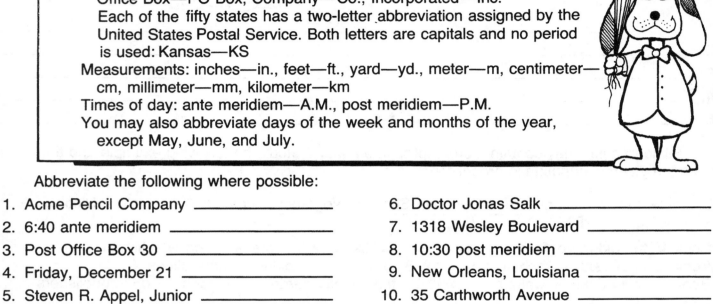

Harry's hints:

An **abbreviation** is a shortened form of a word. It is often followed by a period. An abbreviation is capitalized if used with a proper noun.

Titles of respect: Mister—Mr., Mistress—Mrs., Doctor—Dr., Reverend—Rev., Junior—Jr., Senior—Sr.

Words in addresses: Street—St., Avenue—Ave., Road—Rd., Boulevard—Blvd., Lane—Ln., Terrace—Terr., Route—Rte., Apartment—Apt., North—N., South—S., East—E., West—W., Post Office Box—PO Box, Company—Co., Incorporated—Inc.

Each of the fifty states has a two-letter abbreviation assigned by the United States Postal Service. Both letters are capitals and no period is used: Kansas—KS

Measurements: inches—in., feet—ft., yard—yd., meter—m, centimeter— cm, millimeter—mm, kilometer—km

Times of day: ante meridiem—A.M., post meridiem—P.M.

You may also abbreviate days of the week and months of the year, except May, June, and July.

Abbreviate the following where possible:

1. Acme Pencil Company _____
2. 6:40 ante meridiem _____
3. Post Office Box 30 _____
4. Friday, December 21 _____
5. Steven R. Appel, Junior _____

6. Doctor Jonas Salk _____
7. 1318 Wesley Boulevard _____
8. 10:30 post meridiem _____
9. New Orleans, Louisiana _____
10. 35 Carthworth Avenue _____

Write three sentences, using abbreviations of at least two of the following words in each sentence.

| Mister | Road | Company | Doctor | feet | Pennsylvania |
| Avenue | Monday | October | yard | meter | Washington |

1. _____

_____

2. _____

_____

3. _____

_____

Complete the puzzle below by abbreviating each word.

ACROSS
 5. doctor
 6. route
 7. Friday
 9. avenue
10. apartment
12. centimeter
14. Saturday

DOWN
 1. boulevard
 2. junior
 3. mister
 4. December
 8. inch
11. post office
13. Mississippi

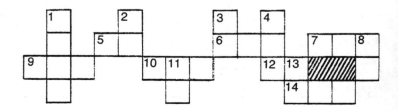

Name _____ Date _____

Harry's hint:
   Addressing an envelope is the same for both a friendly letter and a business letter. Follow several simple rules and your letter will reach its destination quickly.
   1. Include the address of both the **sender** and the **receiver**.
   2. Follow the rules for capitalization and punctuation.
   3. Write neatly and in the proper order.

Harry received this envelope in the mail from his good friend, Hannah Hound. Hannah has followed the correct capitalization and punctuation rules for addressing an envelope. Notice that the **two-letter state abbreviation** is used on the envelope. Both letters are capitalized and no period follows the abbreviation.

SENDER'S
ADDRESS

Miss Hannah Hound
1234 Haversham Place
Pittsburgh, PA 15221

RECEIVER'S
ADDRESS

Mr. Harry Hound
7475 Hanover Rd.
New York, NY 10002

On the lines at the right, rewrite the addresses correctly.

26 Briar Hill farms
Albany, new york 12205
John jensen

Mr. Irwin Cohen
The Ernst research company
Brewster,ma 02631

jacksonville, Fl. 32216
miss Candice Cooper
1690 jefferson ROAD

maggie O'reilly
81001 Pueblo, CO
1621 Hanley Rill

Mr. Manuel ibarra
Almeza ave. 7252
CA La puente 91747

Use another piece of paper as an envelope. Write your school's address as the sender's address and your home address as the receiver's address.

Exclamatory words and **phrases** express strong feeling. They end with an **exclamation mark**. Change the following declarative sentences to exclamatory sentences or phrases by adding or subtracting words.

Example: The mountain path was steep and winding. What a steep path!

1. The Ganges is a very long river.

_____

2. A large quantity of rice is grown each year.

_____

3. There are several floating markets near the city of Bombay.

_____

4. Elephants are lavishly decorated and draped for parades.

_____

5. The Himalayas are very beautiful mountains.

_____

Underline the **interjections** in the list below. Use an **exclamation mark** after each interjection. Write other interjections on the blanks.

1. Hurrah   3. Table   5. Wow   7. Whoops   9. Hurray
2. Glass   4. After   6. No   8. Fire   10. Great

_____   _____   _____   _____   _____

A sentence that asks a question is an **interrogatory sentence**. It ends with a **question mark**. Write a question for each of the answers given below.

1. _____
Tea leaves are picked every two weeks.

2. _____
Air India Airline is owned by the government.

3. _____
Pottery and ivory carvings are the traditional handicrafts.

4. _____
The world's largest filmmaking industry is centered in Bombay.

5. _____
Sri Lanka is off the southern tip of India.

Three of the following groups of words are sentences, and two are fragments. Rewrite each sentence using proper punctuation and capitalization. Rewrite each fragment as a question.

1. the friendly mountain climbing guide

_____

2. how long is this mountain trail

_____

3. will these backpacks be too heavy for James

_____

4. picks and shovel in the sack

_____

5. have you climbed this peak before

_____

Name _____   Date _____

A **declarative** sentence tells something. An **imperative** sentence requests or demands something. An **interrogative** sentence asks a question and an **exclamatory** sentence shows great excitement.

You are about to take a tour of Stonehenge. Label the guide's remarks as declarative, imperative, interrogative, or exclamatory sentences. Add the necessary end marks.

_____ 1. Welcome to Salisbury Plain in the south of England

_____ 2. I will be your guide to the wondrous Stonehenge

_____ 3. Much mystery still surrounds this ancient wonder

_____ 4. Do not disturb the stones or grounds in any way

_____ 5. How many of you are in England for the first time

_____ 6. Pay attention to the two types of stones making up the bulk of Stonehenge

_____ 7. Do you notice the outer ring of thirty massive pillars, some weighing as much a forty tons

_____ 8. These stones probably were hauled from a quarry twenty-four miles away

_____ 9. A theory suggests the stones were hauled on log sledges, while teams of men pushed and pulled

_____ 10. It took over 1,000 men to do the job

_____ 11. Notice the ring of smaller rocks within the main circle

_____ 12. Is anyone familiar with bluestones

_____ 13. Are they not a beautiful color

_____ 14. These five-ton stones can be found no closer than 250 miles

_____ 15. The shaping and contouring of the stones is another matter

_____ 16. One theory suggests that wedges were pounded into the rocks, and cattails were stuffed into the cracks and set on fire

_____ 17. Cold water was thrown on the fire, and this change of temperature caused the rock to split

_____ 18. Remember that Stonehenge was completed with no wheels, no horses, and no metal tools of any kind

_____ 19. Does anyone know when the structure was built

_____ 20. Using the highly accurate carbon 14 dating method, scientists have found that Stonehenge was built around 1800 B.C.

_____ 21. It took over 300 years to complete the project

_____ 22. This was an extraordinary feat

_____ 23. As you gaze about, do you wonder why Stonehenge was built

_____ 24. Most theories involve a study of early astronomy

_____ 25. Let's move on with our tour

EXTRA!
Pretend you are a tour guide for any place in the world. Write down the name of your tour location. Now give your tour group some instructions using the four types of sentences: declarative, imperative, interrogative, and exclamatory.

Name _____ Date _____

Tell whether each sentence is **declarative**, **interrogative**, **exclamatory**, or **imperative**. Put the correct end punctuation mark in the parentheses.

_____ 1. I found it difficult to sleep that Tuesday evening before my thirteenth birthday ( )

_____ 2. Must I really walk Elizabeth to school tomorrow ( )

_____ 3. You should be ready to leave on time in the morning ( )

_____ 4. The crash of glass and a low rumbling sound filled my room ( )

_____ 5. Was someone shaking my bed, or was it just my imagination ( )

_____ 6. It was an earthquake ( )

_____ 7. Get out of the house ( )

_____ 8. The violent shaking continued for over a minute ( )

_____ 9. As we stood dazed and crying, my father called out our names to see if we were all safe and uninjured ( )

_____ 10. What was the eerie orange light coming from our neighbor's parlor ( )

_____ 11. When my father saw the flames, he bolted across the lawn toward the burning house next door ( )

_____ 12. You stay with the girls ( )

_____ 13. Fill containers with water and bring them outside ( )

_____ 14. Can you girls help your mother carry the buckets ( )

_____ 15. My brothers raced back and forth with the buckets of water we had carried to the door ( )

_____ 16. Something was wrong ( )

_____ 17. There was no more water ( )

_____ 18. As we stood in the grass watching the flames, I wondered if anyone remembered it was my birthday ( )

Change these sentences to the type suggested in parentheses. Add correct punctuation.

1. The San Francisco earthquake was in 1906. (Interrogative)

_____

2. Did the fire rage for more than three days? (Declarative)

_____

3. The earthquake destroyed the water pipes that serviced the city. (Interrogative)

_____

4. Get those looters away from that store. (Exclamatory)

_____

5. Could you help put out that fire? (Imperative)

_____

6. Two-hundred thousand people were forced to spend the night at Golden Gate Park. (Interrogative)

_____

7. Were eighty percent of the buildings of San Francisco destroyed in the earthquake? (Declarative)

_____

EXTRA! ∙∙∙
Write an account that may have been written by some experiencing the San Francisco earthquake. Make a draft of your composition from which you can write your final copy.

Name _____   Date _____

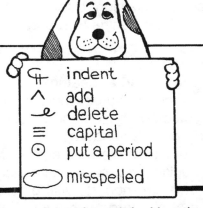

Harry's hints:
Proofreading begins by asking several questions:
Are paragraphs indented?
Are spellings correct?
Are sentences complete?
Do all sentences begin with a capital letter?
Is the end punctuation correct?

⌐ indent
∧ add
℮ delete
≡ capital
⊙ put a period
◯ misspelled

It is important to write your best and make no mistakes when applying for a job. Use the proofreading marks to make corrections on the application below. Rewrite the application correctly on the lines at the right.

HOSPITAL VOLUNTEER APPLICATION

Date: june 9 1989   _____

Name: molly h layton   _____

Address: 7 taylor estates   _____

City, State, and ZIP Code: _____
dallas texas 75201

HOSPITAL: st vincent   _____

2435 couch avenue   _____

fort worth texas 76105   _____

Proofread a craft recipe. The directions must be clear and easy to follow. Use the proofreading marks at the top of the page.

Dough Ornaments

First you need 4 cups flower, 1 cup salt, 1½ cups warm water mix in a bowl with a fork untel it can be shaped into a bal. On a surface dusted with flower knead the dough with the palm of yur hand until it becomes smooth and soft. if it is sticky, add more flower. shape the ornaments by making diffrent size balls and attaching them together with a small amount of water. Bake your ornaments at 250 for about 2 hours or untel hard. decorate with colorfull pens. They can be sprayed with a clear hobby spray to preserve them

Write your own paragraph describing how to make or do something.

Jean has just written a note to her friend, Ann. In her haste, she forgot to watch her capitalization. Use the proofreading mark to show that the name of a **particular place** begins with a **capital letter**.

> a make
> ≡ a
> capital
> letter

Dear Ann,

We landed at heathrow airport near london this morning at 8:00 A.M. Our first stop was at the ritz hotel, where we checked into a beautiful room. It overlooks picadilly square. We could see buses and cars. The dome of st. paul's cathedral is also large enough to be seen from the window.

Tomorrow we will begin sightseeing. Tina wants to visit the tower of london. I want to see buckingham palace and also feed the ducks on the thames river.

Later we hope to visit oxford university and perhaps see a play near Shakespeare's home at stratford-upon-avon. If there is still time, we will go by train to see nottingham and sherwood forest. I wonder if there are any robbers left there? It is great to be in "merrie olde england."

                                        Love,
                                        Jean

Rewrite Jean's letter correctly on a separate paper.

Write a short paragraph describing buildings and streets in your neighborhood. Use at least three street names and two building names.

_____

_____

_____

_____

_____

_____

Write a proper noun in each blank.

1. A particular city in Mexico is _____ .
2. A particular street in New York City is _____ .
3. A particular building in Washington, D.C. is _____ .
4. A particular river in the United States is _____ .
5. A particular country in South America is _____ .

Write an **S** on the line in front of the sentence if the word in boldfaced type names a **particular section** of a country. Rewrite the word to begin with a capital letter in the blank at the end. Write a **D** if the word names a direction. Directions are not capitalized.

___ 1. Another large airport lies **south** of London. _____

___ 2. There are still small villages in the **midwest**. _____

___ 3. The **west end** is a good place to find restaurants. _____

___ 4. Scotland's mountains appear as one drives **north**. _____

___ 5. Wales lies **west** of England. _____

Name _____ Date _____

The reporter who wrote the following story was careless. The editor wants you to use the proofreading marks to make corrections. Combine fragments or add them to existing sentences to make 17 complete sentences. Do not add any words. Rewrite the story on a separate paper.

	make lowercase
ℓ	delete
⊙	make a period

MAN SURVIVES 76 DAYS AT SEA

April 21, 1980
Steven Callahan was rescued today by three fishermen after 76 days at sea His boat was Drifting to shore a few miles off a small island near Guadeloupe. Callahan was in. A tiny, inflatable raft. His cruiser capsized. Near Tenerife On February 5.

Callahan had a small amount of food. And water. He survived by eating raw fish. He had A spear gun in the raft. He was able to spear dorados. And triggerfish. He also caught a bird and a few tiny crabs and shrimp to eat. A small amount of fresh water. Came from a solar still.

The bottom of the raft. Was bumped frequently by dorados and sharks. Callahan was. Able to knock them away with a paddle.

At least six ships Passed close enough for him to see the sailors on board. They did not notice his five-foot raft.

Steven Callahan lost 44 pounds during the ordeal He was. Covered with saltwater boils and unable to walk when he reached shore. Doctors predict a full recovery. In six weeks.

Steven Callahan kept a diary during his 76 days at sea. With limited paper and pencils, he may have used many fragments to keep a record of his adventures. Make these fragments into sentences he might have written. You may use them anywhere in the sentence.

1. alone at sea

_____

_____

2. began to taste much better

_____

_____

3. the sight of land

_____

_____

4. a four-inch hole in the raft

_____

_____

5. a passing ship

_____

_____

Imagine you are lost at sea. Your ship capsizes in a storm. You have time to gather twelve items and throw them into your tiny raft. What would you take? List your survival tools in the first entry of an imaginary diary you keep during your days at sea.

A junior-high student was asked to write a story for class. Use the proofreading marks to correct his errors.

⊙ make a period
a̲ make a capital letter
∧ add
ℓ delete
◯ check spelling

THE NIGHT THEY GOT ME
by Tommy Hartman

I'll never forget the day it was September 2 1987 and I was leaving my friends house. We had just finished and evening swim. There was a full moon that night and i noticed a ring around it. I've herd a lot of really strange stories about the ring around the moon.

I started for home from Bernies house. I had a strange feeling someone or something was, watching me. I continued on my way. I had just gone down the hill when I heard something growl. It was extremely dark and I couldn't see not a thing. I told myself to calm down. I didnt know or even have an idea what it was. I thought the only thing them could have been was a dog, a very big dog.

I started to bak up slowly and, again, it started to growled. It sounded like it was walking in front of I. I walked about ten feat to where I could see the street light. Then all of a sudden the animal jumped in the middle of the street. I couldn't see it real close but I could tell it was on all four's and really hairy. It was making the stranger sound I had ever heard. I started to walk slowly backwards and contued to increase speed. Then I turned and ran up the hill. It was still following me! In fact it was got closer?

I reached a freind's house at the top of the hill, and all my buddies were laughing and rolling on the ground. I turned to look to see if the animal was still after myself. To my surprise, there was my friend Bernie. He was wearing his old halloween costume!

Do not use more than one **negative** word in a sentence. In addition to contractions using **not**, these words are used as negatives: **no**, **none**, **never**, **nobody**, **nowhere**, and **nothing**.

When there is already one negative word in a sentence use **any** in place of **no** or **none**, **ever** in place of **never**, **anybody** in place of **nobody**, **anywhere** in place of **nowhere**, and **anything** in place of **nothing**.

In the following sentences, underline the correct word in the parentheses.
1. Can't the rescuers think of (anything, nothing) to do to help?
2. Aren't you (ever, never) going back to camp?
3. Marie has (no, any) time to think about shopping for the party.
4. Let's not do (anything, nothing) to upset her.
5. Don't you want to go (anywhere, nowhere) for summer vacation?
6. You know why I don't want to see (anybody, nobody) now.
7. I haven't gone (anywhere, nowhere) without a heavy coat.
8. There have been (any, no) storm clouds from the west.
9. Don't you have (anything, nothing) to carry?
10. I don't (ever, never) want to do that again!

Do not use a **negative** word in the same sentence with **hardly**, **barely**, or **scarcely**.
Example of incorrect usage: I **couldn't** hardly hear the whisper.
Correct usage: I **could hardly** hear the whisper.

In the blanks in front of each of the following sentences, write a **C** if the negative word is used correctly. Write an **I** for incorrect usage.
___ 1. I can't scarcely see in this dark cave without a lantern.
___ 2. We can barely lift these large stones.
___ 3. There wasn't hardly any room to walk along the ledge.
___ 4. The rope was scarcely long enough to reach the water.
___ 5. He wasn't barely breathing when we got to him.
___ 6. There was hardly enough room to pull him up.

Write two sentences using each word correctly.
hardly _____
_____
barely _____
_____
scarcely _____

In the blanks in front of each of the following sentences, write a **C** if the usage is correct or an **I** if it is incorrect.
___ 1. The *Blue Fish* isn't no ordinary ship.
___ 2. It has a powerful motor below that no one never sees.
___ 3. It doesn't look like anything but a sight-seeing cruiser.
___ 4. But it doesn't never just leave the dock for pleasure.
___ 5. It will go anywhere within 50 miles to look for trouble.
___ 6. No one would never know that it is a Coast Guard lookout ship.

EXTRA!
On a separate paper, write a short story about an imaginary person who had almost nothing in his or her childhood. Use some of the following phrases in your story: never enough food, no one listened, hardly warm, nothing stopped her, scarcely anything.

Name _____ Date _____

List the following European countries in alphabetical order:
Portugal, France, Italy, Switzerland, Netherlands, Spain

1. _____ 3. _____ 5. _____
2. _____ 4. _____ 6. _____

Alphabetize the words in each of the following groups:

1. Belgium, bell, believe, belt, belong

_____ _____ _____ _____ _____

2. Denmark, dentist, den, denim, dense

_____ _____ _____ _____ _____

3. Norway, north, normally, nor, northern

_____ _____ _____ _____ _____

4. Sweden, sweet, swerving, sweater, swept

_____ _____ _____ _____ _____

5. England, engineer, engage, engrave, English

_____ _____ _____ _____ _____

6. Germany, gerund, germ, geranium, gerbil

_____ _____ _____ _____ _____

Divide the italicized words into syllables by drawing vertical lines. Use a dictionary.

1. Paris, the *capital* of France, is an *increasingly popular* city for *vacationers*.
2. Many Italian *restaurant* owners serve *spaghetti*, *lasagna*, *cannelloni*, *ravioli*, and other pasta to their *customers*.
3. *Potato famines* in Ireland forced many Irish to *emigrate* to *distant countries*.
4. *Liechtenstein*, one of the smallest countries in *Europe*, uses *Switzerland's telephone*, telegraph, and *postal* systems.
5. Many people in *Austria* still wear the *traditional* costumes of heavily *embroidered trousers* and dresses.

Use the dictionary to find the meaning of the words in boldfaced type in the following sentences. Choose a definition that fits, and copy it in the blank after each sentence.

1. The British rock group checked into the hotel's finest **suite**.

_____

2. That night the band played a **medley** of old favorites.

_____

3. The lead singer was very **feisty**.

_____

4. The guitar player was far more **docile**.

_____

5. This was one of the best rock **premiers** the city had ever known.

_____

Use the dictionary to answer the questions about the words in boldfaced type.

1. From which language does the word **marsupial** come? _____
2. From which language does the word **haiku** come? _____
3. What is the proper noun for **polestar**? _____
4. What is the sound of "ti" in **nasturtium**? _____
5. Is a **jardiniere** an ornamental pot? _____

Name _____ Date _____

The volumes in a set of **encyclopedias** are listed alphabetically and usually have a number on the spine.

Using the alphabetical listings, which volume would contain information on the following subjects?

1. Arizona ___   5. Killer Bees ___   9. Habits of the Raccoon ___
2. Transportation ___   6. Eleanor Roosevelt ___   10. Exotic Birds ___
3. History of the Red Cross ___   7. English Channel ___   11. Oliver Wendell Holmes ___
4. Albert Einstein ___   8. World War I ___   12. Planets ___

Articles in the encyclopedias are also listed alphabetically.

Alphabetize the subjects in each column in the order in which they would be found in the encylopedia.

Spanish Art	_____	Pyramids	_____
Tennyson, Lord Alfred	_____	Spain	_____
Ibsen	_____	Mining Gold	_____
Water	_____	Peace Corps	_____
North Pole	_____	Battle of the Bulge	_____

Cross references (other titles and information on the subject), are found at the end of an encyclopedia article.
Example: Christopher Columbus; cross reference—Isabella

List a possible cross reference for each of the following subjects.

1. Niagara Falls _____
2. Outback _____
3. General Robert E. Lee _____
4. Alps _____
5. Printing _____
6. Tornadoes _____
7. Beatrix Potter _____
8. Declaration of Independence _____
9. Spanish Armada _____
10. Computers _____

Using the subject "Grand Canyon" or a subject of your own choice, prepare a reference list from an encyclopedia for a report on the chosen subject.

Articles
_____
_____
_____

Cross references
_____
_____
_____
_____

Any other sources
_____
_____
_____

Name _____ Date _____

Read the following sentences. Then, on the lines below, select and write the correct sentence for each mathematical formula.

Example: noun + conjunction + noun + helping verb + verb + preposition + noun =
Tina and Ronnie were going to school.

1. Neither Tomás nor William could see the serious error.
2. Can you bake a cherry pie?
3. Marta, Jamal, and Terry took a ride.
4. The boy likes that girl.
5. He looks nice in a suit.
6. They are really good to us.
7. Men, women, children, and babies usually like chocolate.
8. She is quietly playing in the yard.
9. Wow! Whose car is that?
10. Solomon worked and played.
11. I work well under the pressure.
12. Come here or I will leave.
13. Joel and Gina were eating the tasty pizza.
14. Janell and Shundrea were working.
15. We waited, but he never came.

1. article + noun + verb + demonstrative pronoun + noun = _____

2. personal pronoun + helping verb + adverb + verb + preposition + article + noun = _____
_____

3. personal pronoun + linking verb + adverb + adjective + preposition + personal pronoun =
_____

4. proper noun × 2 + conjunction + proper noun + verb + article + noun = _____
_____

5. interjection + interrogative pronoun + noun + linking verb + demonstrative pronoun = _____
_____

6. helping verb + pronoun + preposition + verb + article + adjective + noun − preposition = _____
_____

7. 9 nouns ÷ 3 + conjunction + noun + adverb + verb + noun = _____
_____

8. pronoun + verb + adverb + preposition + article + noun = _____

9. pronoun + verb + adjective + preposition + article + noun = _____

10. 2 × subject + predicate = _____

11. subject + 2 × predicate = _____

12. independent clause + conjunction + independent clause = _____

13. correlative conjunction + subject × 2 + predicate + article + modifier + object = _____
_____

Write three different sentences to fit the following formula:
Proper noun + adverb + past tense verb + preposition + article + synonym for "pretty" + noun

ENGLISH REVIEW

Following the usage directions in parentheses, write answers to the questions. Underline the word or words in the answers that show the correct usage.
Example: Who was Louis XIV? (Pronoun as subject)
Answer: <u>He</u> was King of France.

1. In what city or town do you live? (pronoun as object of preposition)

   _____

2. Whom did Helen see at the restaurant? (pronoun as object of verb)

   _____

3. Who gave the gloves to Jack? (singular pronoun)

   _____

4. What were too large? (plural pronoun)

   _____

5. Whose mailbox received the invitation? (possessive pronoun)

   _____

6. Where would they hike? (preposition)

   _____

7. How was the money divided? (use preposition "between")

   _____

8. Where did the senior team go? (prepositional phrase as adverb)

   _____

9. What kind of snake moved quickly? (prepositional phrase as adjective)

   _____

10. What two players were on the hockey team? (conjunction)

    _____

11. Where do oranges grow? (conjunction connecting phrases)

    _____

12. What kind of soldier would never disobey? (adjective phrase)

    _____

13. Where did the horse plunge? (adverbial phrase)

    _____

14. Have you ever eaten Spanish olives? (negative sentence)

    _____

15. Who is your favorite television personality? (appositive)

    _____

16. What did you give him? (direct object)

    _____

17. Where can you find information on Helen of Troy? (determiner)

    _____

18. Where does the path go? (reverse order)

    _____

19. Can you get along without it? (contraction)

    _____

20. What is a homophone for pier? (homophone)

    _____

HARRY'S FAVORITE PUZZLE

Our favorite hound, Harry, has designed a crossword puzzle as a review of English grammar. Good Luck!

ACROSS

2. plural of child
4. plural of ox
5. the simple predicate in the sentence: He jumped over the hurdle.
8. words that are similar in meaning
9. plural of boy
10. use of happy to compare two nouns
13. a sentence that is incomplete
15. opposite of subtract
16. word that means the opposite
17. a word that describes a noun
18. a shortcut way of writing two words, using an apostrophe
21. plural possessive of boy
24. comparison of smart between two nouns
25. a word part added to the beginning of a root word
26. a person, place, or thing
27. without joy
28. the simple subject in the sentence: The hockey player was a good skater.
29. an action word

DOWN

1. the plural of goose
3. a word that sounds the same, but has a different meaning and spelling
6. meaning ownership
7. a sentence that makes a statement
11. plural of story
12. a word that answers how, where, or when
14. a sentence with too many thoughts
17. punctuation used in possessives
19. word abbreviated Thu.
20. punctuation used to indicate a pause
22. word abbreviated yd.
23. plural of knife

Page 3

common nouns, <u>proper nouns</u>
1. face, <u>United States</u>, bill, <u>George Washington</u>
2. president, <u>Mount Vernon</u>, man
3. person, troops, <u>Revolutionary War</u>
4. portrait, bill, <u>Gilbert Stuart</u>
5. artist, portraits, president
6. portrait, <u>Athenaeum</u>

concrete nouns, <u>abstract nouns</u>
1. George Washington, <u>faith</u>, country
2. <u>power</u>, king
3. <u>truth</u>, farm
4. <u>honesty</u>, parents, Augustine, Mary Washington
5. <u>dangers</u>, <u>years</u>, <u>presidency</u>
6. George Washington, school, Virginia, <u>seriousness</u>, <u>studies</u>
7. <u>Revolutionary War</u>, General Washington, <u>respect</u>, troops
8. <u>strategies</u>, <u>war</u>
9. stories, <u>honesty</u>, <u>strength</u>
10. Henry Lee, commander, <u>war</u>, <u>peace</u>, hearts, countrymen

Page 4

<u>Common nouns</u>, **proper nouns**
Susan, **John**, **Midtown Movie Theater**, <u>matinee</u>, <u>walk</u>,
Forest Park, <u>animals</u>, **St. Louis Zoo, Labor Day**, <u>crowd</u>,
<u>animals</u>, <u>chimpanzee show</u>

1. Mississippi River
3. New York
5. Thanksgiving
8. September
10. Abraham Lincoln
11. Mexico
12. Saturday
16. NBC Network
18. Jimmy Carter
19. France

ACROSS
1. FORD
3. WASHINGTON
6. FEBRUARY
9. PHILADELPHIA
12. BELGIUM
13. VALENTINES
14. OAKLAND
15. PACIFIC

DOWN
2. ONTARIO
4. THURSDAY
5. ANTARCTICA
7. INGALLS
8. MISSISSIPPI
10. LABRADOR
11. KANSAS

Page 5

1.-8. Answers will vary.
1. river
2. country
3. continent
4. city
5. king
6. desert
7. sea
8. language

<u>proper nouns</u>, common nouns
1. <u>Queen Nefertiti</u>, woman
2. <u>Egyptian Museum</u>, treasures
3. <u>Royal Scribes</u>, favorites, court
4. <u>Thebes</u>, city
5. <u>Rosetta Stone</u>, key, language

1. Suez, ships
2. Cairo, city
3. Camels, Sahara

1. Ministry of Foreign Affairs
2. Museum of Modern Art
3. Arab Republic of Egypt
4. Aswan High Dam
5. Nile River Valley

Page 6

1. circuses
2. babies
3. flowers
4. lunches
5. skies
6. pennies
7. dresses
8. dishes
9. stories
10. hobbies

1. houses
2. churches
3. shelves
4. butterflies
5. holidays

1. mouse
2. woman
3. goose
4. moose
5. man
6. tooth
7. foot
8. ox
9. sheep
10. swine

Page 7

1. Camel taxis carry tourists miles to the many oases.
2. Thieves have stolen much treasure from ancient Egyptian tombs.
3. The children wrote on papyrus with brushes.
4. Egyptians built their cities on the shores of the Nile River.
5. Artisans carved beautiful ornamental boxes with knives.
6. Horses, geese, sheep, and ducks were kept on the farm by Egyptian families.

1. the lady's hair
2. the ladies' hair
3. the Kings' valley
4. the Sphinx's head
5. the craftsmen's art
6. the hero's death

	Sing. Poss.	Plural	Plural Poss.
1.	desert's	deserts	deserts'
2.	quarry's	quarries	quarries'
3.	woman's	women	women's
4.	dynasty's	dynasties	dynasties'
5.	flood's	floods	floods'
6.	document's	documents	documents'

Page 8

plural, rule #
1. moofs or mooves, 6
2. mnoars, 1
3. porays, 3
4. xummies, 4
5. glifs, glives, 6
6. shilps, 1
7. glishes, 2
8. sofips, 1
9. voxes, 2
10. quiffs, 6
11. poys, 3
12. nobos or noboes, 1
13. glites, 1
14. mercats, 1
15. molios, 5
16. wertwezes, 2
17. bobios, 5
18. chissinies, 4
19. pruffies, 4
20. quives, quifes, 6
21. wuses, 2
22. pirpays, 3
23. sliffs, 6
24. troagies, 4

plurals
1. some men from outer space!
2. trying to catch deer to take aboard his spaceship.
3. brothers-in-law will help me if I decide to board the ship secretly.
4. I got cold feet, I found a good hiding spot.
5. were quiet as mice when we tiptoed aboard the craft.
6. alien added cupfuls of an unknown substance to the tank.
7. ships rose in the sky, I could see women and children below us.
8. started to fear for our lives.
9. alien creatures may not like stowaways.
10. could make friends with the creatures on this trip, we would be heroes.

Page 9

1. John's sweater
2. the boy's fish
3. the teacher's chair
4. the dog's collar
5. the ocean's shore

1. flowers' petals
2. cars' horns
3. cows' milk
4. uncles' pipes
5. cameras' lenses
6. children's toys
7. ladies' purses
8. pens' points
9. horses' saddles
10. brothers' books
11. puppies' bones
12. bears' dens
13. benches' legs
14. bikes' wheels
15. shelves' edges
16. axes' handles
17. youths' games
18. eggs' yolks
19. ostriches' feathers
20. mothers' pies

SINGULAR POSSESSIVES:
town's   skeleton's
neighbor's   house's
doorbell's   neighbor's

PLURAL POSSESSIVES:
trees'   Perkins'   witches'
monsters'   candles'

Page 10

1. dogs, dog's, dogs'
2. ladies, lady's, ladies'
3. kites, kite's, kites'
4. birds, bird's, birds'
5. babies, baby's, babies'
6. peaches, peach's, peaches'
7. geese, goose's, geese's
8. girls, girl's, girls'
9. turkeys, turkey's, turkeys'
10. families, family's, families'
11. candies, candy's, candies'
12. churches, church's, churches'
13. dishes, dish's, dishes'
14. foxes, fox's, foxes'
15. women, woman's, women's
16. sheriffs, sheriff's, sheriffs'
17. mice, mouse's, mice's
18. stories, story's, stories'
19. keys, key's, keys'
20. children, child's, children's
21. boys, boy's, boys'
22. knives, knife's, knives'
23. boxes, box's, boxes'
24. thieves, thief's, thieves'

Page 11

1. A   3. C   5. C   7. C
2. A   4. A   6. A   8. A

1. truthfulness   6. failure
2. quickness   7. silliness
3. honesty   8. faintness
4. illness   9. helpfulness
5. pleasure   10. happiness

abstract nouns: importance, joy name, remembrance, day, ties, chores, generations

concrete nouns: boys, school, scrolls, brushes, boys, paints, pigments, stone, water, paint, boys, school, scribes, jobs, clerks, letter-writers, paymasters, government

1.–10. Answers will vary.

Page 12

appositives
1. a church that opposed war or any type of violence
2. the United States Military Academy
3. the daughter of a wealthy meat packer
4. Brigadier General Fox Connor
5. the date the Japanese attacked Pearl Harbor
6. a plan to invade Europe
7. later called D-Day
8. disbanding the armed services
9. Crusade in Europe
10. governor of Illinois

1. no appositive
2. Explorer I
3. developed by Jonas E. Salk
4. no appositive
5. a proposal to pool resources about atomic information for peaceful uses

1. Dwight Eisenhower, nicknamed "Ike," was elected by a landslide in 1956.
2. The St. Lawrence Seaway, a man-made waterway to the interior of North America, was opened in 1959.
3. Alaska and Hawaii, the 49th and 50th states of the Union, joined the United States in 1959.

Page 13

appositive, **noun**
1. the quarterback, **George Martlin**
2. a tall bronze statue, **trophy**
3. the new librarian, **Mrs. Hartzfeld**

4. the home of George Washington, **Mt. Vernon.**
5. a mean-looking beast, **hound**
6. our cousins, **Kim Ling and Su Yung**
7. a martial art, **Karate**
8. the lawyer on the case, **Mr. Dwyer**
9. our next-door neighbor, **Wileys**
10. an ancient mausoleum, **site**

1.–10. Sentences will vary.

Answers may vary.
1. John's wife,
2. a pink species,
3. Veronica Birney,
4. the tax assessor,
5. the town's landmark,
6. a fine speaker,
7. a graduate of Harvard,
8. the author,
9. a competent woman,
10. known as Sparky,

Page 14

Leonardo da Vinci was one of Italy's finest artists. Leonardo painted a very famous picture of a woman. The woman is known as Mona Lisa. People have studied Mona Lisa's face for years. Still there is a puzzle about Mona Lisa. Who was Mona Lisa? Is Mona Lisa really smiling in the picture? Why? Only Leonardo could answer all of these questions. As far as we know, Leonardo never did.

1. them   5. She
2. It   6. them
3. They   7. him
4. it

It: Colosseum   They: lions
They: spectators   Them: cages
They: races

1. he, him   5. she, her   9. it
2. they, them   6. it   10. they, them
3. it   7 he, him; she, her
4 it   8. she, her; he, him

Page 15

antecedent, **pronoun**
1. John and Philip, **They**
2. Beth, **She**
3. store, **It**
4. sweatshirt, **It**
5. Cher and Elizabeth, **They**
6. School Week, **It**
7. festival, **it**
8. display, **It**
9. gardens and fountains, **They**
10. items, **They**

1. they   1. I
2. it   2. me
3. he   3. I
4. she   4. me
5. they   5. I

Page 16

1. I   6. we
2. they   7. he
3. he   8. It
4. she   9. I
5. you   10. I

1. me   6. him
2. correct   7. correct
3. them   8. her
4. correct   9. correct
5. correct   10. correct

Page 16 (continued)

1. him	6. them
2. them	7. him
3. him	8. her
4. her	9. him
5. him	10. it

them, They, it, It, them, They, them

Page 17

1. S, We	6. O, her
2. S, we	7. S, they
3. S, she	8. S, I
4. O, us	9. S, It; O, us
5. S, you	10. O, us; S, we

1. They
2. He
3. them
4. him
5. He or She

Subject, personal pronoun
1. <u>Miss Wilson</u>, She
2. <u>class</u>, They
3. <u>Edward</u>, He
4. <u>Mairin and Bethany</u>, they

Page 18

1. P	5. S
2. P	6. P
3. S	7. S
4. P	

1. they, them	6. they, them
2. he, him	7. it
3. he, him; she, her	8. it
4. they, them	9. they, them
5. she, her	10. it

1. his	6. his
2. her	7. Her
3. Her	8. hers/mine
4. his	9. his
5. theirs	10. his/her/my

Page 19

1. our	6. our
2. Its	7. My
3. hers	8. Our, their
4. theirs	9. her
5. my	10. their

possessive pronouns that come before the noun,
<u>possessive pronouns that stand alone</u>

1. **her**, <u>mine</u>	3. **his, my**	5. **my**, <u>theirs</u>
2. **our**	4. **My, her**, <u>ours</u>	

1. Her   2. their

Page 20

1. We
2. you, us
3. We, her
4. She, they, mine
   <u>We</u>, <u>you</u>, <u>us</u>, <u>We</u>, <u>her</u>, <u>She</u>, <u>they</u>
5. someone, you, our
6. few, us
7. Something, that
8. you, everyone
   <u>someone</u>, <u>few</u>, <u>Something</u>, <u>everyone</u>
9. These, your
10. this, that, she
11. Those, I
12. you, that
   <u>These</u>, <u>this</u>, <u>that</u>, <u>Those</u>, <u>that</u>
13. It, itself
14. You, yourselves

15. I, myself, you, yourself
16. Your
   <u>itself</u>, <u>yourselves</u>, <u>myself</u>, <u>yourself</u>
17. those, who, I
18. What, you
19. Which, you
20. whom, you
   <u>who</u>, <u>What</u>, <u>Which</u>, <u>whom</u>
21. These, who
22. which, I, hers
23. I, which, my
24. whose, I
   <u>who</u>, <u>which</u>, <u>which</u>, <u>whose</u>
25. our
26. you, yours
27. My, his
28. its, it's
   <u>our</u>, <u>yours</u>, <u>My</u>, <u>his</u>, <u>its</u>

Page 21

ACROSS

2. theirs	13. you	18. her
5. possessive	14. she	19. yours
7. ownership	15. they	20. object
12. contractions	17. me	21. hers/ours

DOWN

1. mine	6. it	11. them
2. their	8. he	14. subject
3. us	9. linking verb	16. your
4. apostrophe	10. him	20. our
5. predicate		

Page 22

1. an	6. a	11. a
2. a	7. an	12. a
3. an	8. a	13. an
4. a	9. an	14. a
5. an	10. a	15. a

1. I	5. D	9. D
2. D	6. I	10. D
3. D	7. D	
4. I	8. D	

1. three, first	4. One	7. first
2. Five	5. fifty	8. Four
3. fourth	6. twentieth	9. two

1. this	5. X	9. this
2. X	6. these	10. X
3. this	7. this	11. these
4. these	8. X	12. X

Answers may vary.

1. His	5. its	9. his
2. our	6. Her	10. your
3. my	7. his	
4. our	8. our	

Page 23

1. untightened: loosened
2. misunderstood: wrongly understood
3. repeated: said it again
4. cooperated: worked together
5. unlocked: opened the locks

1. speller: one who spells
2. joyless: without joy or joyful: full of joy
3. playful: eager to play or playable: able to be played
4. mixable: can be mixed or mixer: one who mixes
5. foolish: like a fool
6. colorful: full of color *or* colorless: without color

elevator–lift	cellar–basement
policeman–bobby	sack–poke
gasoline–petrol	hero–submarine
trunk–boot of a car	flue–chimney

Page 24
1.–6. Answers will vary.

1.–3. Answers will vary.

Answers may vary.
1. transportation, transgress, transpire
2. anticlimax, antidote, antiseptic
3. monotone, monocle, monologue
4. unlike, unnecessary, unhappy
5. portable, portage, porter

suffix, root
1. ness, firm
2. ance, appear
3. ly, real
4. ment, pave
5. ning, begin

Answers may vary.
frost:	frosted, frostily
color:	colorful, colorless
collect:	collected, recollect
port:	transport, report
press:	pressed, repress
appear:	appearance, appeared
want:	wanted, unwanted
count:	countless, recount
last:	lastly, lasted
firm:	firmly, firmness

Page 25
isn't	couldn't	shouldn't
aren't	wouldn't	mustn't
wasn't	won't	weren't
hasn't	haven't	doesn't
don't	can't	you're
they're	she'll	you'll
I'll	I'm	I've
he's	she's	that's

1.–4. Answers will vary.

1. couldn't
2. won't
3. wasn't
4. haven't
5. weren't
6. aren't
7. can't
8. don't
9. isn't
10. doesn't
11. shouldn't

Mystey word (Contraction)

1. It's
2. Their
3. your
4. They're
5. You're
6. Its

Page 26
| she is | I am | you have |
| it is | they had/would | I will |

| I've | they'll | it's |
| he's | you're | we'd |

1. you've (you have)
2. we'd (we had)
3. he's (he has)
4. you'll (you will)
5. I've (I have)
6. she'll (she will)
7. I'll (I will)
8. he's (he is)
9. he'd (he had)
10. it's (it is)

We're, We are
it's, it is
we'll, we will
She's, She has
It'll, It will
We've, We have

1.–5. Answers will vary.
1. It's
2. it's
3. its
4. You're
5. your

Page 27
action verbs:
1. studied
2. are known
3. started
4. ate
5. dominated
6. preyed
7. were protected
8. lived
9. have learned
10. fought

action verb, direct object:
1. discovered, facts
2. laid, eggs
3. study, fossils
4. have learned, reasons
5. caused, seaways

1.–5. Answers will vary.

Page 28
1.–12. Sentences will vary

1. ate
2. swept
3. give
4. sit
5. stands
6. surrounds
7. swim
8. hit
9. climbed
10. scampered
11. peered
12. clapped

1.–8. Answers will vary.

Page 29
verbs: was, imagine, lighten, remain, seize, looks, appear, work, became

1.–5. Answers will vary.

action verbs, verbs of being
1. sailed
2. was
3. played, danced
4. equipped
5. worried
6. assured, was
7. glided, warned, were
8. appeared
9. collided, were
10. covered
11. inspected, called
12. was
13. played, boarded
14. developed, began
15. scrambled, get, was
16. hit, dove
17. leaped
18. became
19. saw, die
20. arrived, survived
21. claimed

Page 30
helping verb, main verb
1. was, known
2. had, developed
3. was, sold
4. was, created
5. had, made
6. were, treated
7. was. opposed
8. had, decided
9. had, established
10. had, moved

sentences with helping verb:
2, 3, 4, 6, 8, 9, 10

Page 31
1. Being, is
2. Being, were
3. Being, was
4. Senses, seemed
5. Being, is
6. Senses, appeared;
   Being, was
7. Being, was
8. Being, was
9. Senses, seemed
10. Senses, feels

Page 32
1. wears, is wearing, wore, has worn, will wear
2. steals, is stealing, stole, has stolen, will steal
3. knows, is knowing, knew, has known, will know
4. sees, is seeing, saw, has seen, will see
5. eats, is eating, ate, has eaten, will eat
6. drives, is driving, drove, has driven, will drive
7. sings, is singing, sang, has sung, will sing
8. freezes, is freezing, froze, has frozen, will freeze
9. rings, is ringing, rang, has rung, will ring
10. goes, is going, went, has gone, will go
11. writes, is writing, wrote, has written, will write
12. says, is saying, said, has said, will say
13. thinks, is thinking, thought, has thought, will think
14. swims, is swimming, swam, has swum, will swim

15. tears, is tearing, tore, has torn, will tear
16. takes, is taking, took, has taken, will take
17. flies, is flying, flew, has flown, will fly
18. chooses, is choosing, chose, has chosen, will choose
19. grows, is growing, grew, has grown, will grow
20. rides, is riding, rode, has ridden, will ride

1. Present, see
2. Past Participle, have thought; Past, were
3. Future, (will) ride
4. Present Participle, is stealing
5. Past, knew

Page 33

1. cheer	6. studies
2. dives	7. practice
3. swim	8. hurries
4. know	9. buzzes
5. watches	10. talks

1. S, begins	6. S, looks
2. S, wish	7. S, prepares
3. S, cheers	8. S, fusses
4. S, volunteers	9. S, cheers
5. P, try	10. P, taste

1. The young girls swim for Sugar Tree Swim Club.
2. The diving coach disciplines the squad with early morning practices.
3. The flags fly briskly over the finish line.

Page 34

1. liked, 2	6. hurried, 3
2. scrubbed, 4	7. handled, 2
3. destroyed, 1	8. swapped, 4
4. studied, 3	9. talked, 1
5. zipped, 4	10. married, 3

Add **ed**
		Drop **e**, add **ed**	
dashed	rested	stared	baked
bloomed	laughed	chased	admired
passed	spelled	lined	hoped
		exploded	tied

Change **y** to **i**, add **ed**
buried	worried	hurried
carried	applied	replied
tidied	cried	married

add **ed**
grabbed	tapped	scrubbed
slipped	batted	

Page 35

1. will bring	3. will have	5. will work
2. will use	4. will shop	

verb, future tense
1. **study**, will study
2. **programs**, will program
3. **type**, will type
4. **have**, will have
5. **corresponds**, will correspond
6. **learn**, will learn
7. **operates**, will operate
8. **appears**, will appear
9. **publishes**, will publish
10. **edits**, will edit

1. Present Participle	7. Past
2. Past Participle	8. Past
3. Present	9. Present Participle
4. Future	10. Past
5. Present Participle	11. Past
6. Past	12. Past Participle

Page 36

1. present, was	6. present, are
2. past, had	7. present, are
3. present, was	8. past, have
4. present, is	9. past, had
5. past, had	10. past, had

Page 37

past, past participle, present participle
1. baked, (have) baked, (is) baking, (past) baked, (present participle) are baking
2. waved, (have) waved, (is) waving, (present participle) are waving, (past) waved
3. marched, (have) marched, (is) marching, (past participle) have marched, (present participle) are marching
4. painted, (have) painted, (is) painting, (past) painted, (present participle) are painting

1. rang, (have) rung, (is) ringing, (past) rang, (past participle) had run
2. led, (have) led, (is) leading, (present participle) are leading, (past participle) have led
3. went, (have) gone, (is) going, (past participle) hade gone, (past) went

verb, verb tense
1. sprang, past
2. is bursting, present participle
3. have traveled, past participle
4. Has caught, past participle
5. wrapped, past
6. is crying, present participle
7. has waded, past participle
8. Is rising, present participle
9. rang, past
10. strike, present

Page 38

1. talks, is talking, talked, has talked, will talk
2. paints, is painting, painted, has painted, will paint
3. prints, is printing, printed, has printed, will print
4. crawls, is crawling, crawled, has crawled, will crawl
5. cleans, is cleaning, cleaned, has cleaned, will cleaned
6. opens, is opening, opened, has opened, will open
7. cooks, is cooking, cooked, has cooked, will cook
8. pitches, is pitching, pitched, has pitched, will pitch
9. plays, is playing, played, has played, will play
10. works, is working, worked, has worked, will work
11. stops, is stopping, stopped, has stopped, will stop
12. turns, is turning, turned, has turned, will turn
13. bats, is batting, batted, has batted, will bat
14. fixes, is fixing, fixed, has fixed, will fix
15. looks, is looking, looked, has looked, will look
16. watches, is watching, watched, has watched, will watch
17. washes, is washing, washed, has washed, will wash
18. smells, is smelling, smelled, has smelled, will smell
19. smiles, is smiling, smiled, has smiled, will smile
20. enjoys, is enjoying, enjoyed, has enjoyed, will enjoy

1. Present Participle, were fixing; Present, hear
2. Past, glanced
3. Past, turned
4. Past Participle, had turned; Present Participle, was making
5. Past, saw; Present Participle, was covering
6. Future, will find; Present, walk
7. Past, moved; Past Participle, were pitched
8. Present Participle, was getting

Page 39

Past	Past Participle
1. filed	filed
2. hurried	hurried
3. sailed	sailed
4. marched	marched
5. destroyed	destroyed
6. poked	poked
7. rushed	rushed

Past	Past Participle
1. rode	ridden
2. lost	lost
3. swang	swung
4. came	come
5. showed	shown
6. won	won
7. ate	eaten

1. went   5. flown
2. drank   6. hid
3. Did   7. known
4. closed

Page 40

1. is   6. will be
2. are   7. was
3. am   8. will be
4. was   9. was
5. was   10. were

1. are   6. is
2. is   7. will be
3. is   8. is
4. is   9. are
5. are   10. will be

Page 41

1. lay   1. correct
2. laid   2. set
3. Lie   3. set
4. lay   4. sat
5. lain   5. correct

1. leave   teach
2. leave   learn
3. Let   Learning
4. left   taught
5. let   learned

Errors in paragraph: (5 errors total)
laid–second sentence (lay)
sit–third sentence (set)
lie–fourth sentence (lay)
let–seventh sentence (left)
learn–eighth sentence (learned)

Page 42

Answers will vary.

1. for   6. to
2. through   7. by
3. in   8. from
4. at   9. with
5. behind   10. on

1. lunch, packages
2. rules, guide
3. camera, shoulder
4. picture, it
5. sound, water
6. sat, riverbank
7. filled, ham and cheese
8. part, day
9. branch, nest
10. moment, film

Page 43

1. to   6. at
2. at   7. at
3. at   8. to
4. to   9. at
5. to   10. to

correct preposition
1. between   6. between
2. Among   7. between
3. among   8. among
4. between   9. between
5. among   10. among

1. besides   4. beside
2. beside   5. Besides
3. Besides

1. from   4. from
2. off   5. off
3. off

correct preposition:
1. into   4. in
2. in   5. in
3. into

Page 44

1. at   6. Before
2. near   7. into
3. in   8   inside
4. in   9. beside
5. by   10. above

Prepositional phrases, **object**
1. around the **park**
2. across the **river**
3. with colorful **stripes;** near our **balloon**
4. by the small **space**; inside the **gondola**
5. from our vantage **point**
6. After an **hour**

Page 45

prepositional phrase, word modified
1. in Africa, mountain
2. of wild animals, Herds
3. of gold, Shipments
4. of rain, amount
5. of the colorful, birds
6. with many rapids, Rivers
7. into the jungle, Safaris
8. of animals, paintings
9. of vicious dogs, Packs
10. from many countries, Visitors

1.–6. Answers will vary.

prepositional phrase, word modified
1. into the compounds, drove
2. to the nearest campsite, walked
3. in the forest, found
4. at dinnertime, helped
5. on the spit, turned
6. around the campfire, raised
7. on the nearby trees, shone
8. out of sight, stayed
9. in their sleeping bags, slept
10. above them, shone

1. A   6. A
2. P   7. A
3. P   8. P
4. A   9. A
5. P   10. P

Page 46
1. quicker, quickest (1)
2. longer, longest (1)
3. meaner, meanest (1)
4. rarer, rarest (2)
5. higher, highest (1)
6. wider, widest (2)
7. sillier, silliest (4)
8. bigger, biggest (3)
9. flatter, flattest (3)
10. more expensive, most expensive (5)

1. biggest
2. larger
3. longer
4. sillier
5. hotter
6. lowest
7. hungrier
8. heaviest

Page 47
1. pen, America's, best, well-known
2. real
3. humorous, ordinary
4. newspaper, cub, adventurous, riverboat
5. pen, riverboating, safe, twelve, deep
6. four, spectacular
7. good
8. first, famous, white-washed
9. runaway
10. enormous, fascinating

Page 48
2 tame game
8 brave knave
6 fat gnat
7 pale quail
1 crazy daisy
9 slick chick
10 found sound
5 spare pair
3 round hound
4 fine swine

Page 49
1. Danish
2. German
3. French
4. Belgian
5. Canadian
6. Chinese
7. British
8. Swedish
9. Spanish
10. South American

1. The Alaskan art was on display in the museum.
2. The British tea was served with cream and sugar.
3. The Liberian freighter steamed into port.
4. The Asian flu is making many persons ill.
5. American food is more plain than French cuisine.

Page 50
Adjectives:
Japanese, many, ancient, special, tall, colorful, toy, flying, one, six, six, old, brave, strong

1. tall   2. brave, strong   3. toy, flying

festivals: many, ancient
way: special
custom: old

Adjectives: Japanese, special, favorite, beautiful, tiny, doll, pretty, delicious

1. tiny, doll
2. delicious

favorite: friends
pretty: display
beautiful: dresses

Page 51
adjectives
1. bad
2. poor
3. nice
4. small
5. red
6. mean
7. dirty
8. good
9. funny
10. empty

adjectives in letter:

paragraph 1–our, incredible, more, German, various
paragraph 2–daily, ideal, Every, wooden, vaulting, prison, old, Red Cross, packing, Long, wooden, four, strong, its, dusty, exercise
paragraph 3– solemn, vaulting, trap, arduous, sandy, appointed, yellow, two, tedious, pulley, constant, any, tunneling, slight
paragraph 4– escape, two, this, microscopic, long, hooded, black, dark, coffee, remaining, noisy, our, sudden, no, free, our, loved
complimentary closing–Your

Page 52
unnecessary words in sentences:
1. here
2. there
3. there
4. here
1. factory
2. salesperson
3. keys
4. tires
1.–8. Sentences will vary.
1. A
2. N
3. N
4. A

Page 53
Comparative	Superlative
1. bigger	biggest
2. greener	greenest
3. longer	longest
4. faster	fastest
5. younger	youngest
6. happier	happiest
7. later	latest
8. more wonderful	most wonderful
9. more difficult	most difficult
10. more honest	most honest

1. largest, S
2. faster, C
3. highest, S
4. most important, S
5. more popular, C

1. bad, worse
2. nice, nicest
3. messier, messiest
4. large, larger
5. good, best

Page 55
adjective phrase, noun modified
1. of extraordinary power, king
2. at Versailles, palace; of lasting beauty, building
3. of the French Revolution, years
4. of the French Army, general
5. of his troops, Members
6. of silk, manufacture
7. of high style, dresses
8. of fashion, leader
9. among dress buyers, stir
10. of fashion design, business

1. Soldiers of great courage crossed the Alps.
2. The path up the mountain was very steep.
3. Roads of concrete would have been helpful.
4. Generals must be leaders with strength.
5. The house of green was a rendezvous point.

Page 56
1. sweetly
2. colorfully
3. crossly
4. dryly
5. lightly
6. stuffily
7. rapidly
8. blankly
9. wisely
10. sharply

Page 57
1. soon, when
2. quickly, how
3. below, where
4. smoothly, how
5. closely, how
6. Sometimes, when
7. well, how
8. overhead, where
9. Afterwards, when
10. after, when

Page 58

1. back and forth
2. inside
3. under
4. everywhere
5. upward

adverbs: beginning, up, top, top, far away, nearby, here, there, down

1. climbed the mountain
2. received the prize
3. took a chance
4. read the books
5. slept
6. danced
7. recommended
8. laughed

Page 59

adverb, word modified, word modified (part of speech), question answered

1. frequently, left, verb, when
2. quickly, spoke, verb, how
3. too, quickly, adverb, how much
4. nowadays, understand, verb, when
5. finally, happy, adjective, when
6. down, swooped, verb, where
7. easily, won, verb, how
8. quite, gracefully, adverb, how much
9. gracefully, dances, verb, how
10. totally, inappropriate, adjective, how much

adverb, word modified

1. eerily, quiet
2. never, freezes; certainly, enough, cold
3. usually, black, thick
4. occasionally, report
5. only, late; mysteriously, vanishes
6. apparently, surfaced
7. seldom, talked
8. quickly, spread
9. actually, studied
10. suddenly, saw
11. immediately, grabbed
12. then, were published; anywhere, available

Page 60

1. more intensely
2. best
3. most carefully
4. more efficiently

later   latest
better   best
more badly   most badly
more joyfully   most joyfully

stiff, stiffer, stiffest
casually, more casually, most casually

Page 61

1. over
2. away
3. up
4. down
5. often

Answers may vary.
1. quickly
2. backward
3. immediately
4. profusely

adverb, verb
1. Yesterday, forgot
2. never, borrows
3. always, brings
4. Suddenly, rang

Page 62

adjectives, adverbs
1. young, quickly
2. thick, closely
3. quiet, momentarily
4. large, then
5. metric, carefully
6. interested, nearly
7. next, math, metric, later
8. last, clearly
9. metric, customary, amazingly
10. next, enthusiastically

Answers may vary.
1. tall
2. intelligent
3. five
4. plastic
5. glass

1. quickly
2. inside
3. tomorrow
4. later
5. easily

Page 63

1.–10. Sentences will vary.
1.–10. Sentences will vary.

adverb phrases:
in Europe
from region to region
on the Atlantic Coast
with great force
in the water
on the Mediterranean coast
in warm sunlight
In the chateaux country
on rock foundations
with grapes
in some ways

Page 64

g. garbage disposal
e. the wind
d. the chair
a. the candlelight
b. fog
f. the rain clouds
h. wind chimes
c. sirens

1.–5. Answers will vary.
1. elephant
2. mile
3. bucket
4. truck
5. steam
6. ears
7. rock
8. star
9. teacher
10. sky

Page 65

1. Crimson, swept
2. Grim, exhausted, struggled
3. crashed, heavily
4. Startled, fled
5. splash, hissing

1.–9. Answers will vary.
1. precipitous
2. lovable
3. ravenous
4. comforting
5. cozy
6. cautious
7. penniless
8. miserable

Page 66

1. pain, suffering
2. freedom
3. ready to fight
4. unplanted, dormant
5. drawn out

1.–5. Answers will vary.

trip: pilgrimage, journey
again and again: repeatedly
told: bade

Page 67

1. S	6. S
2. A	7. S
3. A	8. A
4. S	9. S
5. A	10. A

antonyms:	synonyms:
1. late	1. entertaining
2. long	2. leaped
3. freezing	3. scampered
4. boring	4. knocked
5. hard	5. silly
1. dry	6. tall
2. slow	7. brave
3. win	8. cry
4. star	9. sad
5. love	10. down

Page 68

1. their	6. There
2. correct	7. correct
3. there	8. They're
4. There	9. There
5. their	10. their

1.–10. Sentences will vary.

1. scene	9. allowed
2. hole	10. flower
3. know	11. scent, sent
4. mane	12. isle, I'll
5. rowed/road	13. heed
6. one	14. son
7. groan	15. principal
8. plain	

Page 69

threw	rain, piece	stare
hear, through	feet	

1.–5. Sentences will vary.

tale	scent	patients	steak
principal	pane	pear	

1. My feet were sore as I tried on my new pair of shoes.
2. I ate a piece of carrot.
3. I have never seen a prettier beach than this one.
4. Our principal lost his patience over the tale we told.
5. We sent eight students to buy two steaks for our class.

Page 70

1. Peter wanted to ski, but there was no snow in England today.
2. He called the tourist office, and he asked about snow.
3. Switzerland has plenty of snow, but it is far away.
4. Peter could fly to Switzerland, or he could save his money for summer vacation.
5. He decided to go at once, and he bought a ticket.

1. N	4. N
2. P	5. N
3. N	

1.–8. Answers will vary

1. California, Florida
2. milk, tea
3. long, interesting
4. on the beach, in the ocean
5. down the hill, into a snow bank
6. rings, bracelets
7. Marie sang, Jerry played the piano
8. Hal went to the game, Jay stayed home
9. up, over
10. walked, ran

Page 71

subject, predicate (simple/compound)
1. location, is (simple)
2. seismograph, registered/recorded (simple)
3. Seismographs/equipment, were checked/evaluated (simple)
4. quake registered/that...is considered (compound)
5. there, were/this caused (compound)
6. state, was called/United States Forest Service, closed (compound)
7. side, began (simple)
8. Clouds/rain, prevented (simple)
9. Scientists, began/geologist called (compound)
10. Livestock/wildlife, acted/farmers told (compound)
11. Governor Ray, allowed (simple)
12. Harry S. Truman, defied (simple)

1. The explosion on May 18 was heard 200 miles away, and a cloud of steam rose 63,000 feet in the air.
2. Winds were of hurricane force, and they blew down millions of two-hundred-year-old trees.
3. The forest fires were widespread, but the falling ash helped to put out the ensuing fires.
4. Volcanic mudflows, called lahars, flowed down the mountain at 50 miles per hour, and their temperature was 211 degrees F.
5. Everyone realized the ash flowing down the mountain was hot, but few realized the temperature was 800 degrees.

Page 72

1. family/took	4. museums/proved
2. We/stayed	5. guide/told
3. city/was	

1. The flowers bloomed along the sidewalk.
2. The artists painted by the River Thames.
3. The guards stood outside Buckingham Palace.

Page 73

simple subject, **simple predicate**
1. Our class **went** on a field trip to a farm.
2. The bus **left** the school promptly at 9:00.
3. The farmer **was waiting** for us at his barn.
4. First, we **saw** Guernsey cows in the barnyard.
5. The barn **was filled** with the smell of fresh hay.
6. The milking machine **was** very time-efficient.
7. The modern equipment **kep**t the farm working well.
8. In the afternoon, we **went** to the wheat fields.
9. The farmer's wife **had baked** delicious cookies.
10. The entire family **waved** good-bye as we left.

Page 74

1. person	6. thing	11. thing
2. place	7. person	12. person
3. thing	8. place	13. place
4. place	9. thing	14. person
5. person	10. place	15. person

1. smell	6. Happiness
2. visit	7. headlines
3. townspeople	8. wind
4. Ducks	9. Ice
5. Pedro	10. light

1.–10. Complete subjects will vary.

Page 74 (continued)

Aesop's fable: simple subject
underlined within complete subject
A beautiful crystal <u>spring</u>
a large <u>stag</u>
The clear <u>water</u>
His gracefully arched <u>antlers</u>
his funny, spindly <u>legs</u>
The unhappy <u>stag</u>
The strong <u>scent</u> of a panther
The frightened <u>stag</u>
his wide-spreading <u>antlers</u>
The hungry <u>panther</u>
the <u>stag</u>
the despised spindly <u>legs</u>
the graceful <u>ornaments</u> on his head

Page 76

adjective clause, word modified
1. who lives on High Street, girl
2. no adjective clause
3. where they saw the panda, zoo
4. whom everybody cheered, president
5. no adjective clause
6. that I finally repaired, couch
7. that Jane wanted to see, movie
8. no adjective clause
9. that Jose brought to the studio, band
10. no adjective clause

Answers may vary.

1. crossed the bridge
2. counted votes
3. had tears in her eyes.
4. slammed shut
5. chewed on a bone
6. pressed her skirt
7. was ready first
8. picked a team

Page 77

1. S	3. F	5. F	7. S
2. F	4. F	6. S	8. S

1. The lineman was put into the penalty box for fighting. He was very angry.
2. The machine that makes the ice on the rink was brought on because the ice was melting. It was a very warm day.
3. We decided to stay for the whole game. It was a very long game due to many fights and penalties.

Ice hockey is a popular sport played around the world. **I**n Canada **t**he game began in the early 1990s. In order to keep the game moving quickly, players are substituted while the game is in progress. The action can include fights among players. **T**he players need to be very good skaters. **T**he games are played **i**n three 20-minute periods.

Page 78

1. S	6. F
2. F	7. F
3. S	8. S
4. F	9. S
5. S	10. F

1. A	6. A	11. B
2. B	7. B	12. A
3. A	8. A	13. A
4. B	9. B	14. A
5. A	10. B	15. B

Sentences will vary.
transformed, writhed, stretched, stare, outwitted, slashed, crashed

Answers may vary.
1. was   4. stole
2. sailed   5. was
3. tried

Page 79

1. declarative	6. imperative
2. interrogative	7. interrogative
3. exclamatory	8. declarative
4. exclamatory	9. interrogative
5. imperative	10. exclamatory

Page 80

1. looked, N	6. kept, N
2. stood, R	7. does flow, R
3. is, R	8. looked, N
4. lay, N	9. has, N
5. sat, R	10. rested, R

1. suspect	6. view
2. tracks	7. noise
3. footprints	8. coat
4. clue	9. chase
5. corner	10. suspect

1.–10. Sentences will vary.

Aesop's fable: <u>direct object</u> underlined within complete predicate
stood on the kitchen table.
was wide, was narrow.
asked his <u>mother</u> for some nuts.
nodded her <u>head</u>.
took an extra large <u>fistful</u>.
was not able to get his hand out of the narrow top.
began to cry.
came to the rescue.
told <u>him</u> to be satisfied with half of the nuts he had grabbed.
could pull his <u>hand</u> out again.
could get more <u>nuts</u> later.

Page 81

Topic Sentences:
1. The automobile show is entertaining and informative.
3. Christmas is a special time of year.
6. The cast met in the gymnasium for play practice.

Answers may vary.

Topic sentences:
Gary was getting ready for the game.
Carlos prepared for class.
A storm was approaching the city.
Sentences will vary.

Sentences that do not relate to topic sentence in paragraph at bottom of page:
A bright blue rag rug covered the kitchen floor.
The sun shone brightly through the window.
The birds were singing outside.

Page 82

1. The streets of many large cities in China are lined with shops.
2. <u>One type</u> is small shop that sells food and bright, colored cards.
3. <u>In addition</u>, the shop is a library.
4. <u>First</u>, customers pay the shopkeeper a small amount of money.
5. <u>Then</u> they are allowed to sit on the floor and read.

Page 83

Answers may vary.
1. a building
2. photographic equipment
3. clothing/footwear
4. a flower/plant
5. a beverage
6. timepiece/jewelry
7. something to read
8. way to travel in the snow

Page 84

254 Deer Creek Road
Lawrence, Kansas 66044
March 17, 1990

Dear Tim,

(Body of letter)

Lots of luck,
John

1257 Martinville Street
Lima, Ohio 45804
May 3, 1995

Dear Holly,

(Body of letter)

Love,
Marie

Page 85

Learning to Play the Piano
I. Early skills
  A. Learning to read notes
  B. Practicing scales
    1. Major scales
    2. Minor scales
II. Intermediate skills
  A. Learning tempo
  B. How to use metronome
  C. Learning fingering
III. Advanced skills
  A. Interpretation
  B. Styles of different composers
    1. Classical
    2. Modern

Sports
I. Team Sports
  A. Volleyball
  B. Football
  C. Baseball
  D. Soccer
II. One or two player sports
  A. Chess
  B. Tennis
  C. Golf
  D. Ping-Pong

Page 88

1. three
2. cargoes of different ships
3. oars
4. The first carries exotic things, and the last carries less
costly, fewer, useful things.
5. Palestine, wine
shores, moidores
days, trays
6. the English Channel
7. cargo—goods carried on a ship
haven—harbor, port
galleon—heavy sailing ship
amethyst—purple stone
sandalwood—wood used in carvings and cabinetwork
isthmus—a narrow strip of land connecting two larger land areas

Page 89

1. M	6. P
2. P	7. S
3. P	8. S
4. P	9. P
5. M	10. M

Page 91

The following words should be capitalized:
1. Jenny Perkins, Matthew Street
2. Tuesday, February
3. My, I, United States Post Office
4. Halloween, Thanksgiving
5. Charlotte's Web, E.B. White
6. Doctor John Burns
7. New York City, New York
8. Carol Cobb Cookie Company, County Journal
9. Dear Mrs. Daly
10. Come, Annalise

There, Joan	There, Harry
Who	Who, Halloween
Her	He
But	As
And, Bay Bank	Just, Larry
Garage Sale	House for Sale
September 7, 1989	Open House
976 Woodgate Ave.	Wednesday 10:00
	1414 Tappan Lane
	Cincinnati, Ohio

Valentine's Day Party
Los Angeles City Hall
February 14, 1990

Page 92

1. Dr. R.J. Stone
2. Reverend Hollister
3. policeman
4. Captain Cook
5. Governor Harold Blake
6. Mr. Larry T. Hill
7. Mrs. Mary Haas
8. Professor Judd
9. grocer
10. Aunt Maggie
11. Ms. Helen Tucker
12. little girl
13. Uncle Harry
14. Miss Whitman
15. Major Collins

missing letters (by column):
Frank, **g**overnor, **S**uzie
George, **U**ncle, **H**arry, **D**racula, **M**arvin
Bob, **r**everend, **S**amantha
Joan, **g**irl, **a**ctress, **C/K**athy
Janice, **a**unt, **D/T**ina
Miss, **S**mith

Page 93

1. India is famous for elephants, tea, and the Taj Mahal.
2. The Taj Mahal is a beautiful tomb built with a double
dome, a very high entrance portal, and four corner domes.
3. The building features white marble, red sandstone, and a
lovely garden.
4. The huge monument is decorated with jewels, alabaster
screens, and carved writings from the Koran.
5. Around the outside are four towers or minarets, a lovely
reflecting pool, and a peaceful river.

1.–5. Sentences will vary.

1. meat, potatoes, and eggs
2. books, desk, and teacher
3. geese, wolves, and fox
4. tires, headlights, and brakes
5. drums, guitars, and microphone

1. Answers will vary.
2. Answers will vary.
3. winter, spring, summer, and fall
4. Mercury, Venus, Earth, and Mars
5. Answers will vary.

Page 94

1. (C) Serena Crisp, my friend, is a spelunker.
2. (D) Actually, she is a spelunker and a speleologist.
3. (B) If you investigate a cave for a scientific reason, you are a speleologist.
4. (A) A speleologist investigates caves in winter, spring, summer, and fall.
5. (D) Caving, I believe, is a very physical activity.
6. (A) To explore a cave requires many tools, much patience, and a lot of courage.
7. (B) (A) When Serena enters a cave, she has three sources of light, a hard hat, and sturdy boots.
8. (B) She often takes friends caving, but she makes sure they are well prepared.
9. (A) You can take a boat ride, explore a tunnel, or see unusual stone shapes in Mammoth Cave.
10. (C) Carlsbad Caverns, a cave in New Mexico, is the largest cave in the United States.
11. (A) Names based on the formations include the Throne Room in Wyandotte Cavern, the Parachute in Lehman Cave, and the Christmas Tree in Carlsbad Caverns.
12. (C) Missouri, "the cave state," has nearly 5,000 caves.
13. (A) Cave dwellers include bats, cave fish, and spiders.
14. (C) Serena, will you take me spelunking?

1. bats, water, and mud
2. stalagmites, stalactites, and columns
3. brown, furry bats
4. through the clay, under the water, and over the rocks

Page 95

1.–6., Sentences will vary

1. "And so, my fellow Americans, ask not what your country can do for you, but what you can do for your country," said John F. Kennedy in his Inaugural Address in 1961.
2. President Franklin D. Roosevelt exclaimed as the United States entered World War II, "The only thing we have to fear is fear itself!"
3. "Early to bed and early to rise, makes a man healthy, wealthy and wise," wrote Benjamin Franklin in Poor Richard's Almanac.
4. Neil Armstrong radioed from the moon in July, 1969, "Houston, Tranquility Base here. The eagle has landed."

Page 96

Two strawberries were walking down the street. One strawberry said to the other, "If it weren't for you, we wouldn't be in this jam!"

1. "Do you feel well?" asked his wife.
2. "Yes, I am fine. Why?" he replied.
3. "Well," she said, "you look as though your skin is turning orange."
4. "Orange!" he exclaimed. "Are you kidding?"
5. "Say, you are right! I do look orange!" he laughed.
6. "Perhaps," he told his wife, "living in Alaska for three years has done this. Maybe I am not getting enough sun."
7. The man went to see his doctor. "Doctor," he said, "I seem to be turning orange. Do you have any advice?"
8. "Tell me about your diet. Are you getting enough vitamins?" questioned the doctor.
9. "Well," he replied, "I eat a lot of carrots and yellow vegetables, and I drink a lot of tomato juice."
10. "I know what is wrong," said the doctor. "You are eating too many yellow, orange, and red foods. Stop eating those foods, and you will turn back to your normal color."

Page 97

1. "How the Elephant Got His Trunk" is an amusing story.
2. Sports Illustrated had a good article called "How to Hit a Homerun."
3. "Where Was the Key?" is the most exciting chapter in the book.
4. Mrs. Street made the poem, "The Song of Hiawatha," sound interesting.

1.–5. Answers will vary.

1. Yes
2. No
3. No
4. Yes
5. No
6. No
7. Yes
"BIRCHES"

Page 98

1. Henry Reed's Baby-sitting Service
2. The Call of the Wild
3. Jamie and the Mystery Quilt
4. A Tale of Two Cities
5. Johnny Tremaine
6. The Legend of Sleepy Holllow
7. The Secret Garden
8. Tales of Mystery and Imagination
9. The Diary of a Young Girl
10. North to the Orient

1. Seventeen
2. Ranger Rick
3. Readers' Digest
4. Sports Illustrated
5. Natural History Magazine

1. Cats
2. The Taming of the Shrew
3. The Sound of Music
4. Fiddler on the Roof
5. Arsenic and Old Lace

Page 99

1. Dickens, Charles. Hard Times.
2. Dulles, Allen. Great True Spy Stories.
3. Fraser, Antonia. Mary Queen of Scots.
4. Spicer, Dorothy Glady. The Owl's Nest.
5. Vance, Marguerite. The Lamp Lighters.

1. Sullivan, Harry. The Old Trevor Farm. New York: Wilton Press, 1982.
2. Hill, Richard. Under Sail, Boston: Oldtimer Publications, 1978.
3. Walters, Mary Delaney. The Country Garden. London: Druid Publishers, 1900.

Page 100

1. Acme Pencil Co.
2. 6:40 a.m.
3. PO Box 30
4. Fri., Dec. 21
5. Steven R. Appel, Jr.
6. Dr. Jonas Salk
7. 1318 Wesley Blvd.
8. 10:30 P.M.
9. New Orleans, LA
10. 35 Carthworth Ave.

1.–3., sentences will vary

Mr., Rd., Co., Dr., ft., PA
Ave., Mon., Oct., yd., m, WA

ACROSS		DOWN	
5. DR	10. APT	1. BLVD	8. IN
6. RTE	12. CM	2. JR	11. PO
7. FRI	14. SAT	3. MR	13. MS
9. AVE		4. DEC	

Page 101

John Jensen
26 Briar Hill Farms
Albany, NY 12205

Mr. Irwin Cohen
The Ernst Research Company
Brewster, MA 02631

Miss Candice Cooper
1690 Jefferson Road
Jacksonville, FL 32216

Maggie O'Reilly
1621 Hanley Rill
Pueblo, CO 81001

Mr. Manuel Ibarra
7252 Almeza Ave.
La Puente, CA 91747